THE W STUP~~IDEST~~
STUP~~IDEST~~
Inventions

THE WORLD'S
STUPIDEST
Inventions

ADAM HART-DAVIS

ACKNOWLEDGEMENTS

I am most grateful to Christine Foster, who spent many hours poring over dusty volumes in the glorious dungeons of the old Patent Office, and to Jolyon Troscianko, who drew a number of the pictures.

First published in paperback in Great Britain in 2003 by
Michael O'Mara Books Limited
9 Lion Yard
Tremadoc Road
London SW4 7NQ

Previously published in hardback in 1999 as *Eurekaaargh!*
by Michael O'Mara Books Limited

A CIP catalogue record for this book is available from the British Library

ISBN 1-84317-036-1

3 5 7 9 10 8 6 4 2

Designed & Typeset by Design 23

Printed and bound in Great Britain by Cox & Wyman, Reading, Berks

Contents

Introduction

In 1879 the Rev. George William Garrett designed, built, and launched the world's first powered submarine, which according to a newspaper report was 'very nearly successful'. Unfortunately, very nearly successful is not quite good enough, especially for a submarine, and that is what this book is about.

Inventions are often at the leading edge of technology; enthusiastic engineers believe that it must be possible to build a submarine, a human-powered aircraft or a beautiful new musical instrument. They patent the idea, go ahead and build it, and sometimes it works, but sometimes it doesn't. Good iron and steel became available in the middle of the nineteenth century, along with good steam engines to provide power; the urge to build machines must have been almost irresistible, and that must be one reason why the Victorians seem to have been especially ingenious and diverse in their ideas. Creative engineers in the middle of the nineteenth century must have felt that any sort of machine they could imagine must be not only possible to build but unshakeably successful.

When I started working on this book I was worried that it might be just a list of unlucky duds – and I kept feeling sorry for the person who invented the drink called 6-Up. However, the book seemed to take on a shape of its own, and I found that looking at the limits of possibility provided clues about why some inventions fell outside those limits. Sadly, I have only been able to scratch the surface of the subject; there are millions of failed inventions, and only a select few could get into a book of reasonable size.

I have generally avoided such pieces of technology as the telegraph or the Hansom cab, which were a great success in their day but have simply been superseded. Instead I have chosen particular areas of endeavour, such as flying and cycling, and within these areas have tried to show the great triumphs – the inventions that actually worked, alongside a number of near and not-so-near misses. As you will see, many of these 'failed' inventions were within inches of success – indeed, some did succeed briefly. Others, however, now seem so far from the possibility of working as to be absurd. However, we have the benefit of hindsight – the only exact science.

Adam Hart-Davis

1 Nautical nightmares

Conquering the waves must have been a goal for millions of people, from swimmers and canoe-paddlers to those who designed the world's greatest ships. But lurking for every swimmer and mariner are the desire to go more quickly, and the possibility of disaster …

Swimming machines

Liborio Pedrazzolli was born and raised in Italy and moved to England about 1880. He married a local girl and set up a business at 11 Hoxton Street, London, making and selling mirrors, but he was also a keen swimmer.

I don't know whether he swam in the canal that runs through Hoxton, or in a swimming bath, but he must have been dissatisfied with the pull he was able to exert with his hands, for in 1896 he took out a patent for swimming umbrellas, to be held one in each hand, and the patent explains clearly how they were meant to work:

Pedrazzolli's swimming umbrellas (1896)

8

> **The apparati close when the hands are thrust forward thereby causing but little resistance or obstruction ... but when the return stroke is made the apparati expand in umbrella form, and the resistance thus offered enables the swimmer to pull or propel himself through the water at a speed hitherto impossible...**

These umbrellas are not a disaster. They do open and give you a grip on the water. The problem is that they take about one foot of travel to open – perhaps half a second. By this time your hand is back level with your shoulder, and most of the power of the stroke is gone – used up in opening the umbrella. Meanwhile, every other movement is slightly impeded by holding the umbrellas, so that, although they probably speed you up a little at the end of the stroke, they slow you down all the rest of the time. Maybe I just did not make mine well enough. Perhaps you can do better.

More elaborate, and probably less efficient, is William A. Richardson's Improved Swimming Device of 1880. According to the inventor, transferring the work from the hands and feet to the propeller enables the swimmer to proceed rapidly and easily, at a speed of 4–6 m.p.h. Undaunted by this invention, Gustav Zacher patented in 1899 a closely similar machine with pedals for the feet to

Richardson's 'Improved' Swimming Device (1880)

turn the propellers, and floats to take some of the weight of the apparatus. Mr Zacher claimed that the user could simultaneously swim and pedal:

> **Thus a peculiar double action is produced firstly by the swimmer moving himself forward directly and taking the apparatus with him, and secondly by the propellers driving the apparatus forward and the latter carrying the swimmer along with it. In the consequence of this double action and the essentially greater utilisation of the leg power the swimmer can travel in the water with the apparatus much more quickly than the ordinary free swimmer, or than a person on a water vehicle propelled by him by a treadling motion and screw propellers.**

It sounds to me as though Zacher expected his swimmer to be able to have his cake and eat it at the same time!

The problems I can see with this device are that carrying all that ironmongery about would make me sink instantly to the bottom; the thrashing of the elbows and knees would greatly impede progress; such propellers are hopelessly inefficient below speeds of about 200 r.p.m., which is much faster than the limbs can do under water; and finally, if it did get going, then the spinning of the propeller in one direction would tend to make the body spin in the other direction, which would be most disconcerting.

Life-saving equipment

Those who travelled by boat were always acutely conscious of the possibility of shipwreck, and many precautions were taken to prevent boats from sinking. Surrey engineer Fred Grantham Broughton patented a novel system of providing

Barathon Aîné's propeller-driven lifebuoy (1895)

the ship with a number of airtight tubes extending from the deck down through the bottom of the vessel, these tubes being closed at the top and open at the bottom, so that 'should the vessel, by reason of a leak, collision or any other cause, begin to settle in the water, the air enclosed ... is gradually compressed by the water entering them, the contained air being ultimately compressed to such an extent that the pressure thereof counterbalances the tendency of the vessel to settle, thereby preventing its sinking.'

He also took the precaution of lining the ship with enough cork to keep it afloat even if it was riddled with holes.

The improved suit and fittings for 'Saving Life in Water'(1870)

There seem to be at least a couple of problems with this idea. First, filling the entire ship with air tubes and cork would leave no space for engines, cargo, crew or passengers. Second, he would do better to close his tubes at both ends, since the buoyancy of a parcel of air depends on its volume, and the compressing of the air would actually reduce the buoyancy, rather than increasing it as he supposed.

In general I think I'd rather stay in a regular vessel, but, just in case I do fall overboard, there is a splendid choice of lifebuoys. François Barathon Aîné of Paris patented a magnificent propeller-driven version in 1895 (see previous page). This provided the shipwrecked person with an inflated buoyancy bag to sit on, and had not just one but two propellers – one behind for cruising in search of help, and one below 'to prevent it sinking'. Both these propellers could be driven by pedals, by hand, or both. The shipwrecked mariner was provided with a compass, a small mast and sail, and a lantern to attract the attention of rescuers in the dark, plus 'a drawer enclosing toilet articles and boxes of preserved meat and fresh water'.

Even this luxurious device was a poor relation, however, of Captain John Benjamin Stoner's 'New or Improved Suit or Dress, and Fittings for Saving Life in Water', patented in 1870. The 'india-rubber suit of clothing made large enough to cover the person with all his clothing on', with the addition of an external jacket of cork, was designed to keep you afloat and warm, while 'a cap or hood is attached to the back and upper part of the said suit for covering the whole of the head and neck, except the face...' You were kept upright by lead weights fixed to the ankles. An attached floating hollow buoy provided flares, rockets, a flag for drawing attention to yourself and hand paddles for increasing your speed of swimming, while a floating accessory box contained drinking water, food, cigars, reading matter, a pipe and tobacco, so that when shipwrecked you could enjoy a good meal and a smoke, and read the news to pass the time before rescue – although how the newspapers were to be delivered is not quite clear; nor can I see how you could easily carry all this equipment with you at all times in case of the possibility of shipwreck!

Resurgam

In 1879 the Rev. George William Garrett designed, built and launched the world's first powered submarine, which according to a newspaper report was 'very nearly successful'. I was fascinated to discover the whole story.

George Garrett was born in Dublin and educated at Trinity College. He became a curate in Moss Side, Manchester, and later a commander in the Turkish Navy – but that's another tale. In 1878, while he was at Moss Side, he established the Garrett Submarine, Navigation, and Pneumatophore Company – 'pneumatophore' is a word usually used to describe the air bag jellyfish use for buoyancy – and in 1879 he designed his submarine ...

She was 45 feet (13.7 metres) long, and powered by steam. The boiler was stoked while she was on the surface, and then the fires were damped down and she submerged, using diving rudders. In theory she could stay under water for four hours, and do 10 miles (16 kilometres) at two or three knots. The Navy recognised her potential, and offered Garrett £60,000 if she passed marine trials in Portsmouth.

So he held a parish fête to raise funds, and launched her from Birkenhead. But she ran into a storm just a few miles into her journey; off Rhyl in North Wales the crew were taken off, and the submarine sank. She was called *Resurgam*, which is Latin for 'I will come up again', but unfortunately she never did.

However, the story is not yet over, for at the end of 1997 divers found *Resurgam*, a little rusty but in surprisingly good condition, on the sea bed off North Wales. There are speculative plans to recover her, and active discussion about how to preserve an ageing submarine.

The first submarine?

However, Garrett's was far from being the first submarine. The earliest we know about was apparently built about 1620 by the Dutchman Cornelis Drebbel, who was born in 1572 in Alkmaar, and moved to England at the request of James I. There is no clear contemporary description, but Drebbel's submarine was probably like two rowing boats, the second clamped upside down on top of the first, and the whole thing covered in greased leather. There was a watertight hatch, a rudder and four oars. Under the rowers' seats were large pigskin bladders, connected to the outside by pipes.

When the submarine set off, these bladders were empty

and tied shut with rope. When the crew wanted to dive they untied the rope, allowed the bladders to fill with water, and down she went. When they wanted to surface the crew squashed the bladders flat, squeezing the water out. This was enough to increase the buoyancy, and the vessel rose to the surface.

Drebbel was so satisfied with his submarine that he built two more, each bigger than the last. The final model had six oars on each side and could carry 16 passengers. The hull was strengthened with iron bands, and even had windows. This model was demonstrated to the King and thousands of Londoners. It could apparently stay submerged for three hours and had a range of six miles.

Allegedly the King declined the offer of a personal trip (sensible man!), but according to one account the submarine travelled in three hours the six miles from Westminster to Greenwich and back, cruising 15 feet (4.6 metres) below the surface. This seems unlikely: either the observer had a poor idea of time, or the submariners did not go all the way to Greenwich!

Since Drebbel built three submarines we can guess that they were rather more successful than Garrett's, but the idea of underwater travel does not seem to have resurfaced for a couple of hundred years.

The SS Bessemer

My favourite nautical nightmare was caused by the famous steel magnate, Sir Henry Bessemer. He was a self-made man who started from fairly humble beginnings, but managed to make a sequence of fortunes by putting bright ideas into practice. His first came from a process for producing bronze powder for making 'gold' paint. He discovered that the bronze powder cost seven shillings (35 pence) an ounce,

The industrious Henry Bessemer

whereas the brass from which it was made cost only sixpence ($2^{1}/_{2}$ pence) a pound – more than 200 times less – and he realised there was an opportunity to make a financial killing.

He invented a set of machines to grind brass into powder, had separate parts of the machines made by various companies all over the country, assembled them himself in a private house, kept each machine covered in a separate locked room, and then allowed no one inside the house except his brothers-in-law for 35 years. So he kept the process secret, and without ever taking out a patent made himself a fortune.

He invented a machine with heated rollers for embossing patterns on velvet, a sugar-cane-crushing machine, and the famous Bessemer converter, which allowed the finest steel to be made some 5,000 times faster than had been possible before. Indeed, it allowed mass production of steel for the first time. In order to sell the process to the steelmakers of Sheffield, he set up his own factory there, with offices in Bessemer House, which is still there today.

Henry Bessemer had an idea for spinning artillery shells to make them more accurate. The British Army weren't interested; so he sold it to the French, which meant he had to cross the Channel frequently for consultations.

Unfortunately, Bessemer was a poor sailor, and was seasick on every trip. He wrote:

> Few persons have suffered more severely than I have from sea-sickness, and on a return voyage from Calais to Dover in the year 1868, the illness commencing at sea continued with great severity during my journey by rail to London, and for twelve hours after my arrival there. My doctor saw with apprehension the state I was in. He remained with me throughout the whole night ...

So, when he was financially secure, and his steel business was humming, he set about designing a boat in which he could not be seasick.

He approached this problem scientifically. Boats rock in two directions – they pitch from end to end, and they roll from side to side. The ship he designed was very long, so that she would not pitch, but rather sit across the waves. To eliminate the effect of rolling, he suspended the entire cabin on trunnions, with a huge weight underneath, so that, however much the ship rolled, the cabin would always stay level. In this way he hoped to avoid all the problems and to be able to cross the Channel in comfort.

He built a model of this ship, which was greeted with some scepticism, and then constructed a full-scale replica of the cabin, 20 feet (6 metres) square and weighing several tons, in the field behind his house. It was made to roll through 30 degrees by a steam engine. This seemed to him to be a success, and, although others doubted whether the ship would work at sea, he went ahead and formed the Bessemer Saloon Ship Company, and built the SS *Bessemer*. Her maiden voyage took place on 8 May 1875. She sailed

Anti-seasickness vessel: the SS Bessemer (1875) whose maiden voyage would be her last

majestically from Dover, on a fine calm day, crossed the Channel, and slowly but comprehensively demolished the pier at Calais. The SS *Bessemer* was completely impossible to steer, and she never put to sea again. The Bessemer Saloon Ship Company sank without trace.

2 Tragedies of transport

Horse-drawn carriages

During the eighteenth century most people travelled by foot, although rich people had the option of riding on horseback or using a horse-drawn carriage. These varied from the lightweight racers to the great lumbering stagecoaches, but

Whoa! Annie Howell's 'Appliance for Stopping Runaway Horses' (1899)

none travelled fast because the roads were so terrible.

Nevertheless, horses sometimes became scared, and bolted, and the runaway horse was a serious worry. Annie Howell from South Wales devised a way of stopping runaway horses by suspending a stiff strap between an extra pair of reins, so that when the reins were pulled the strap would press on the horse's wind-pipe, causing him to stop. This sounds rather unkind to me, and in any case it assumes that the driver will still be in position to grab the reins after the horse has bolted, which seems unlikely.

I prefer the hi-tech solution of John Young Walker MacAlister, who planned to mount an extra drum under the vehicle, driven by cogs or friction wheels from one of the axles. An extra pair of stopping reins was to be attached to the drum so that when the apparatus was brought into action the reins would be wound around the drum, pulling the horse's head back and forcing him to stop; the winding action would be released automatically when the horse's head was pulled well in. This still depended on the driver throwing a lever to put the apparatus into action, but presumably he could do this anyway if, for example, he had to get down to deliver something.

Some people designed their own carriages to suit their particular needs. Sir Joseph Banks – the rich fat botanist who sailed with Captain Cook on his first voyage around the world, enjoying a number of amorous encounters with the ladies of Tahiti, and was President of the Royal Society for 42 years – built a vast coach to carry him between his London house and his estate at Revesby in Lincolnshire. One of his long-suffering companions wrote:

> It carried six inside passengers, with much more than their average luggage ... Sir Joseph ... travelled with trunks containing voluminous specimens of his *hortus*

siccus in whitey-brown paper, and large receptacles
for further vegetable matter, which he might
accumulate in his locomotions. The vehicle had ...
several fixed appertenances ... in particular there was
a remarkably heavy safety-chain – a drag-chain upon
a newly-constructed principle, to obviate the
possibility of danger in going down hill, – it snapped,
however, on our very first descent; whereby the
carriage ran over the post-boy, who drove the
wheelers, and the chain of safety very nearly crushed
him to death. It boasted also ... a hippopedometer ...
by which a traveller might ascertain the precise rate
at which he was going ... this also broke, in the first
ten miles of our journey: whereat the philosopher to
whom it belonged was the only person who lost his
philosophy.

Journeys with Sir Joseph were made even slower because
every time he spotted a weed, or a
tree with an unusual branch, he
stopped the carriage and leapt
out, armed with his
magnifying glass and
specimen jars, to
botanise.

Erasmus Darwin,
Charles's grandfather,
was an enormously fat
doctor who lived most
of his life in Lichfield,
Staffordshire, and needed
his carriage to visit his

Erasmus Darwin

patients in the surrounding countryside. He was immensely successful; on one occasion a man came all the way from London to see him for a consultation. Afterwards, Darwin asked him why he had made the long journey, rather than visit the eminent Dr Warren in London. The man replied, 'I *am* Dr Warren.'

Darwin was also popular and conscientious, and spent a lot of time on the road; so he made sure his carriage was convenient and comfortable. On one side of him he always carried a hamper of food in case he got hungry, along with a flagon of water, for Darwin did not drink alcohol. On his other side was a folding desk with books to read, and writing materials. He used to pass the time by writing poetry, which was good enough to impress the poets Coleridge and Wordsworth, and was often concerned with matters scientific, since he was a founder member of the Lunar Society, and a close friend of James Watt and his colleagues.

Newcomen steam engines had been pumping water out of the mines for fifty years by then, and James Watt, prodded by the businessman and manufacturer Matthew Boulton, was talking of using steam engines to drive machinery; so the idea of steam-powered carriages was in the air. But the steam engines they knew were vast, heavy, lumbering beasts, firmly fixed in huge engine houses. To make a mobile steam engine needed new inspiration, and a new step in technology – high-pressure steam, which would deliver much more power for the weight of the engine.

3 Flying fiascos

The first successful balloon flight was achieved by the Montgolfier brothers in 1783, and balloons filled with hot air, hydrogen or helium have been flying about ever since. More recently they have been joined by their more sophisticated siblings, airships. However, balloons and airships can carry only small payloads, or a few people, and they are rather at the mercy of the wind. As a result, people have for hundreds of years tried to follow the birds, by building heavier-than-air flying machines.

Early dreams

Daedalus and his son Icarus, according to the Greek legend, tried to escape from captivity on the island of Crete by flying like birds. They made themselves wings by using wax to stick feathers to their arms, and flew off the island, but Icarus was enjoying the sensation so much he became foolhardy, and flew too high – too close to the sun. The sun's heat melted the wax and he crashed to his death in the sea. According to some modern ideas, Daedalus, who was a canny engineer and the architect not only of the labyrinth but also of King Minos's fabulous palace at Knossos, had invented the hang-glider.

People must always have wanted to fly. Birds look so wonderful as they soar overhead, and watching seagulls and rooks you can easily believe that flying would be easy and fun. Leonardo da Vinci clearly thought so. His notebooks contain detailed sketches of birds in flight under various

This inventor
may well have
spent too long
with his head
in the clouds

conditions of wind and weather, and of a number of flying
machines, powered by hands or feet. None of these was
technically possible around 1500, but Leonardo did not let
impracticality stand in the way of his imagination.

What is slightly surprising, however, is his optimism. He
fully appreciated the size of birds' wings and muscles in
relation to the rest of their bodies, and yet he sketched
human-powered flying machines with wings too small to
support human weight and yet too big to be driven by puny
human muscles.

Flights of fancy did not end with Daedalus and Leonardo.

How about the wonderful vehicle dreamed up in 1885 by an American doctor, W.O. Ayres of New Haven? Ayres must have been impressed if not mesmerised by the power of compressed air. His flying bedstead was to be held up like a helicopter by four propellers mounted on vertical shafts and powered by turbines, driven by compressed air stored in two cylinders. The aeronaut was to sit on a bicycle saddle, control the supply of air with his left hand, and propel the machine forward by driving a horizontally mounted propeller with his right hand. Meanwhile, with his legs he would pedal to assist the lifting rotors. Luckily for the aeronaut, there can have been little danger of this machine leaving the ground!

Batty bedstead-flying machine as dreamt up by Dr W.O. Ayres (1885)

Bird-men

Relatively successful attempts at flying had been made by John Stringfellow and Samuel Henson in 1848, and by Sir George Cayley in 1853. During the second half of the nineteenth century, dozens of intrepid Victorian would-be aviators invented a great array of weird and wonderful flying machines that had about as much chance of flying as lead balloons with heavy anchors in tow. Perhaps they never saw pictures of the Cayley and Stringfellow machines, or perhaps they just ignored all the work that had been done and ploughed their own furrows – literally, in many cases!

One of the most curious of these machines was a 'natural flying machine' proposed by an American in 1865. He had clearly thought about the effort exerted by birds, and wrote from Baltimore suggesting that since a brown eagle can carry off a baby or a lamb, weighing perhaps 20 pounds (9 kilos), then 10 eagles should be able to carry an adult human. He suggested that the eagles should have fitted jackets which would be attached to a circular framework of hollow tubes which in turn would carry a basket, rather like the baskets carried by balloons. He imagined a network of cords passing through the tubes, which would allow the passenger to control the altitude of the machine by compressing or releasing the birds' wings, and a similar system to control direction by swivelling the birds' necks to point the right way. He does not mention such problems as how to persuade the birds to fly at all, nor how to prevent them from plunging to earth if they spied a tempting rabbit or other form of lunch.

Mr W.P. Quimby of Wilmington came up in 1871 with a system so elementary that it is scarcely any advance on the wings of Daedalus and Icarus, except that the wannabe flyer is supposed to be able to help flap by using his leg muscles, since a piece of rope is tied from each ankle to the corresponding elbow. This must be a good idea in principle, since the leg

A seriously bird-brained idea: one inventor's dream of flight (1865)

muscles are much bigger and stronger than those in the arms and shoulders, but my instinct is that the long piece of rope between the wing and the ankle would be more likely to cause some unpleasant dislocation of the hip or one of the leg joints than to allow any useful extra effort to be used for flight. What's more, Quimby's wings must be too small.

Could people fly?

Henson and Stringfellow calculated that a square foot of wing could support half a pound. Let us suppose for a moment that this is about right. Then to support the weight of a light intrepid aviator of say 150 pounds (68 kilos) – just less than 11 stone – the wings would need an area of 300 square feet (28 square metres). Mr Quimby's wings have an area of about 30 square feet (2.8 square metres), which is 10 times too small.

Consider the muscles too. An Olympic gymnast can just support himself for a few seconds by his hands on the rings with his arms straight out sideways. Most of us would be quite unable to do this, and yet to fly upward with a wing on each arm would require greater strength than simply to hang motionless. Therefore our arm muscles are nowhere near strong enough to fly with. We can walk upstairs, and even run upstairs for short periods, but to climb, say, 100 feet (30 metres) in a minute is a major effort even for the powerful leg muscles. So, if a human being is to fly using muscle power, the legs should do most of the work, and the flight can only be slow.

An ingenious and amazingly brave Belgian inventor, Mr de Groof, spent years designing and building what he called a parachute, to imitate the action of birds. His framework was made of wood and rattan and covered with strong waterproof silk. His wingspan was nearly 40 feet (12 metres),

Over in a flap: de Groof's fatal flying-machine (1874)

and the total area of the wings and the tail must have been close to 300 square feet (28 square metres); so at least he was in the right ballpark. He controlled the machine by three hand-operated levers.

For his first trial, he jumped from a great height on to the Grand-Place in Brussels, which was a complete flop, but luckily he escaped unhurt. He then went to London, where a balloonist, Mr Simmonds, took him in his machine to a height of 450 feet (137 metres) and then released him. I am amazed. However confident I was in my theory of flying, I should not be keen, after a crash, to start my second test flight from 450 feet (137 metres) above anything, let alone London! However, de Groof glided safely down and landed in Epping Forest. But on 9 July 1874 he tried again, with fatal results. Mr Simmonds took him up to 1,000 feet (300 metres) and released him, and de Groof's plan was to glide down and land in the Thames. Alas, however, on release the wing frame collapsed, and the courageous de Groof plunged to his death.

One of the most sensible of the human-bird inventions was the flying apparatus of the German Otto Lilienthal. Following in Cayley's glidepath, he studied the flight of birds, and wrote a book about it as a basis for the art of aviation. His apparatus was astonishingly similar to the modern hang-glider, although he had to make the wings of thin osier rods covered with fine linen. In flight they became slightly concave underneath, like the wings of a heron – or a hang-glider. He also fitted a prominent tail fin in order to steer, and reported that on a high, long-distance flight he succeeded in making a turn of 180 degrees, so that he ended up flying in the opposite direction.

At first he jumped with his wings from a high tower on a hill near Berlin, which must have been awkward, but then he moved to a 200-foot-high hill in the Rhinow Mountains near

Neustadt. Of the moment when he first unfolded his wings on the hill, Lilienthal said:

> I was overcome by anxiety at the thought that I was to descend from this height into the wide expanse of landscape which stretched out far beneath me. But the first cautious attempts at diving soon restored me to the consciousness of safety, for I took off much more gently from here than from the tower which was my former launching-point.

He also described vividly the method and sensations of flying:

> With folded wings you run against the wind and off the mountains, at the appropriate moment turning the bearing surface of the wings slightly upward so that it is almost horizontal. Now, hovering in the wind, you try to put the apparatus into such a position in relation to the centre of gravity that it shoots rapidly away and drops as little as possible. The essential thing is the proper regulation of the centre of gravity; he who will fly must be just as much the master of this as a cyclist is of his balance. Obviously, when one is in the air there is not much time to ponder about whether the position of the wings is correct; their adjustment is entirely a matter of practice and experience. After a few leaps one gradually begins to feel that one is a master of the situation ... the aviator ... travels over deep chasms and soars for several hundred yards without the slightest danger, parrying the wind successfully at every moment.

Unfortunately, on 9 August 1896, Otto Lilienthal was testing a new type of steering device, crashed to earth from a height of 50 feet (15 metres), and broke his spine; he died the next day. His last words were said to be 'Sacrifices must be made.'

One idea that definitely escaped de Groof was that there was little point in trying to flap – Cayley had shown that it was not necessary – and therefore there was no point in having two separate wings, since the 'shoulder joints' would come under tremendous stress; much better to rely on a single strong spar from wing tip to wing tip, with no hinge in the middle. Lilienthal's hang-glider may or may not have had such a spar. He talked of his 'wings', but they may have been rigidly fixed together.

The machines of de Groof and Lilienthal were gliders, and not only did they have a reasonable chance of success, having roughly the right area of wing and not expecting too much of the pilot, they both worked to some extent, and their inventors definitely enjoyed real flight. When it came to powered machines, however, many inventors seemed to take leave of their senses, or at least made absurd assumptions about the strength of human muscles.

In 1889 John P. Holmes of Oak Valley, Kansas, dreamed up 'a light and strong machine for navigating the air, designed to be readily controlled by the aeronaut to give the best possible results in flight with the least expenditure of

A hell of a ride: Goupil's flying machine (1885)

Pedalling for the sky (1888).
I doubt it!

power'. The pilot lay on his stomach on a canvas support, steering with his feet, controlling the pitch – that is the angle – of the aeroplane with one hand, and using the other to turn the curious propeller in front. 'The aeroplane is arranged to be rocked up and down, and locked at any desired adjustment, for utilising wind currents and the propelling force of the wind to the best advantage.'

Not only is the wing – perhaps 30 square feet (2.8 square metres) including the tail – far too small to support a human being, but the idea of using only one hand for propulsion is ridiculous: imagine trying to swim using only one hand to pull yourself forward – trying to do pull-ups or climb a rope to beat the pull of gravity.

Mr A. Goupil's aeroplane of 1885 had slightly more chance of getting off the ground, although I would not be keen to put money on it. The wing area is only about 50 square feet (4.6 square metres) (wooden strips covered with silk), but at least Mr Goupil planned to use the leg muscles for power. Cunningly, as the pilot pedals furiously, he turns both the wheel between his feet and the propeller in the nose. Thus, 'as the apparatus obtains velocity its weight diminishes on account of the increase of the vertical reaction of current, and, finally, it ought to ascend and maintain itself aloft …' although in practice I doubt whether it actually did so.

The 1888 pedal-powered helicopter is another optimistic device. Here there is nothing fancy – merely a minimal frame and a large rotor, powered directly by the pedals. Even if the rotor could be 100 per cent efficient, however, trying to lift yourself like this would be like running upstairs at full speed carrying the helicopter, which would need a pilot of exceptional power and stamina. An additional problem is that because of Newton's third law of action and reaction, when the rotor turned anticlockwise the rest of the machine would necessarily spin clockwise, which would be most disturbing, and would probably, within seconds, make the pilot violently airsick.

Theodore A. Stark of Ottawa, Illinois, designed in 1893 a motor turned by both hands and feet:

> thus enabling every muscle in the body to be used to supply the driving power for, say, a flying machine. The flyer lies in a framework of tubes, his feet hook into movable rods, his arms move a second set of rods, and all these movements are transmitted to an endless belt which runs over two pulleys. The motive power is then transmitted from there to the propellers.

All I can say is good luck, Ted Stark! The wing area is perhaps 100 square feet (9 square metres) – so he isn't going to stay up for long. And all those rods and belts and pulleys are going to use up at least half his energy in overcoming friction. I should expect his maiden flight to be mainly downward – and terminal.

So, in their fantasies, the Victorian inventors came close to the modern hang-glider, but they were a long way from achieving human-powered flight, which did not happen until

23 August 1977, when a superfit cyclist and hang-glider expert, Bryan Allen, pedalled his way into the air and round a figure-of-eight course around two markers 800 metres apart, as prescribed, in order to win the Kremer Prize of £50,000.

The aircraft in which he achieved this amazing feat was the *Gossamer Condor*, designed by the aeronautical engineer Dr Paul MacCready. Built from balsawood, cardboard, superthin Mylar plastic film and piano wire, the *Gossamer Condor* weighed only 70 pounds (32 kilos), and yet had a wingspan of 96 feet (30 metres). Since the total weight of the pilot plus the plane must have been between 200 and 250 pounds (90–113 kilos), the wing area of some 500 square feet (46 square metres) was just about in line with the 1840 calculations of Henson and Stringfellow. The pilot steered with his hands and pedalled furiously to turn the propeller using his leg muscles to get lift and propulsion.

The following year Allen flew a slightly more advanced aircraft, the *Gossamer Albatross*, across the English Channel, taking nearly three hours, fighting a headwind, to cover the 23 miles. Since then there have been a number of other human-powered flights, including one of 70 miles, which took four hours.

Engine-powered aircraft

John Stringfellow just managed to achieve flight using a steam engine, but his was an ultra-lightweight steam engine, and his aircraft never took off from the ground: he launched it from a wire. The mill in which it flew is some 25 yards (23 metres) long. He slung a wire from one end to the middle, sloping slightly down, so that once the engine started the aircraft would accelerate down the wire and then launch itself with a simple mechanical trip when it came to the end. In this way he could be sure it would be travelling at flying speed when it first went into free flight, and also travelling dead straight and level, since the aircraft had no tail fin for lateral stability, and the wing tips had only about five feet (1.5 metres) of clearance on each side.

The experiences of Cayley and Stringfellow seem to have passed by Joseph Kaufmann of Glasgow, who in 1869 designed a steam-powered aircraft in the form of a bumblebee. The 40-horsepower steam engine weighed 2.5 tonnes – it would have made a good steam carriage or small railway locomotive. To get this into the air he attached a pair of wings, each 35 feet (10.6 metres) long, which the engine was supposed to flap 120 times a minute. To ensure the stability of the aircraft in flight he suspended a 90-pound (41-kilo) weight underneath, on a long telescopic rod.

Let's just consider the facts. The wing area, assuming the wings were to be 6 feet (2 metres) wide, would have been about 420 square feet (39 square metres), which when gliding would be enough to carry 210 pounds (95 kilos) – but the steam engine weighed 25 times that! No chance of gliding, then. Meanwhile if the wings flapped through an arc of 30 degrees – which is modest, since the wings of most birds and insects flap through at least 90 degrees – the wing

Kaufmann's bumblebee design for a flying machine (1869) did not create a lasting buzz

tips would have to travel at 200 feet (61 metres) per second, or 150 m.p.h. Even worse, they would have to go backward and forward three times a second, reaching this speed on each stroke. There is no material capable of taking such stresses – the wings would break apart in seconds.

Undeterred by such considerations, however, Kaufmann planned a machine with a 120-horsepower engine, which he claimed would be able to carry three gondolas with a few passengers at 56 m.p.h., with fuel for 10 hours and water for three. However, his 40-pound (18-kilo) model, supplied with steam from an outside source, was not a great success. During a demonstration the wings did indeed make flapping movements, but when the steam pressure was increased the wings finally broke, and the model was seriously damaged.

Joseph Kaufmann was not the only one. The Russian Professor Baranowski designed a more futuristic but equally implausible steam-powered aircraft, and apparently demonstrated a model of it at St Petersburg in 1883 (a small model without a steam engine, I suspect!). The cylindrical machine was to take the form of a gigantic bird. The task of

Professor Baranowski's 'gigantic bird' (1883) was another flight of fancy

Maxim's maximum flight was only a second or two (1894)

the powerful steam engine inside was not only to flap the wings but also to drive the three propellers – one in the stern and one under each wing.

Steering was to be achieved by means of oarlike rudders, one each side of the tail. The 'beak' of the bird was to have an opening to allow the ingress of air for the crew to breathe and the fuel to burn, while the escaping smoke and steam would make the huge craft resemble a comet with a luminous tail. And once again there was to be a weight suspended below the machine to keep it properly in balance.

On 31 July 1894, according to *Scientific American*, 'for the first time in the history of the world, a flying machine actually left the ground, fully equipped with engines, boiler, fuel, water, and a crew of three persons.' Unfortunately the proud inventor, Hiram Maxim (famous for his machine gun), 'scarcely had time to realise his triumph before fate, which so persistently dogs the footsteps of inventors, interposed to dash his hopes.'

The Maxim flying machine was a vast structure of steel
tubes and wires, with a maximum of five pairs of wings and a
wingspan of 125 feet (38 metres). The crew stood on the deck
at the bottom, along with the boiler and gasoline. The twin
150-horsepower steam engines, mounted 10 feet (3 metres)
above the deck, each drove a propeller nearly 18 feet (5.5
metres) across. A reporter from the *Pall Mall Budget*
described vividly the scene when both engines were running:

> The platform on which we stood rocked and quivered
> with the vibration. A hurricane seemed to spring up,
> laying the hay flat far and wide, and scattering like a
> whirlwind the shavings in the workshop 20 yards away.
> Every one grabbed his hat with one hand, and clung for
> dear life with the other to the rail.
>
> Suddenly, when the tornado had reached its height,
> and the whole machine was shaking and straining at its
> anchor like a greyhound in the leash, a shrill whistle gave
> the order to 'let go', and the huge structure bounded
> forward across the meadows with a smooth sailing
> motion, at a rate increasing up to 40 miles per hour.

However, although this vast machine flew for a second or
two, it crashed back to earth, embedding its wheels in the soft
grass, and 'in a moment it lay stretched on the grass, like a
wounded bird with torn plumage and broken wings.'

The steam engine, as Cayley and Stringfellow had realised,
could never deliver enough power for an effective flying
machine; that had to wait until the turn of the century, when
the internal-combustion engine became readily available; then
the aviator could indeed get 100 horsepower into a pint pot,
as Cayley had dreamed.

4 Power failures

Blowing in the wind

Windmills were allegedly invented in the Middle East, although probably they and water wheels were dreamed up in various parts of the world. One of the more elegant windmill designs was patented by Benjamin Wiseman Jnr, a merchant of Diss, Norfolk, in 1783. The beauty of this construction was that the direction of the wind did not matter: it would still revolve, like four boats sailing in a circle. The problem was that each sail had to go about and gybe on every revolution, and repeated gybing in a strong wind will tear any sail to pieces; it can even break the mast.

In 1828 the citizens of Bristol were astonished to see a new vehicle, pulled by a kite, sailing along the roads, over the downs, and into the hills. 'After many experiments Mr George Pocock,' according to the *Annals of Bristol*, 'invented a vehicle somewhat similar in form to the modern tricycle, and found that one of these, capable of carrying four persons, could be drawn by two kites of twelve feet and ten feet in height respectively – the speed attained with a brisk wind being about twenty-five miles an hour.' He called his kite-powered carriage a charvolant, and demonstrated one to George IV at Ascot races in 1828.

The *Liverpool Mercury* recorded that Pocock used kites to pull a ferryboat across the Mersey, and said that with the largest kites and a good wind, a boat 'would be able to make the passage from and to Birkenhead, whatever might be the state and strength of the tide', and that the boat could be drawn in any direction 'less than five points from the wind'.

According to Pocock's *Treatise on the Aeropleustic Art, or Navigation in the Air, by means of Kites or buoyant sails, with a description of the Charvolant, or Kite Carriage*:

> Mile after mile, in succession, has been performed at the rate of twenty miles an hour, timing it by chronometer in hand. A mile has frequently been performed, over a heavy road, in two minutes and three quarters. Let it be noticed, that the wind was not furious, neither were the kites additionally powerful for the bad state of the roads ...
>
> That the swiftness of movement should almost prevent breathing, is certain, if going against the wind; but when travelling at such a rate, it is with the wind, and thus a perfect calm is enjoyed. One evil, however, it was supposed did arise from its velocity – loss of appetite; for on one occasion, when pulling up at a house of call seventeen miles from Bristol, some little concern was felt by the party when not one of them was disposed to take any refreshment. ... However ... on looking at the chronometer, they discovered that their travelling pace, up hill and down, had been sixteen miles within the hour: of course there could be little disposition to hunger so soon after a plentiful repast at home.

Could this loss of appetite explain why today's roads are not crowded with charvolants?

Pocock promoted the use of kites for various other things, including rescues. To demonstrate his ideas he put his young daughter Martha in an armchair and flew her up to the top of a high cliff. She survived the ordeal, and went on to become the mother of the cricketer W.G. Grace. However, kites could not provide power to run machinery.

Electricity

Before leaving problematic power, I must just tell you about
Herr Rudolf Diesel's 1897 patent to bring power to balloons.
He proposed to chase after the balloon with a truck running
on electrically charged rails and to supply electricity to the
balloon by using an extension lead hundreds of feet long. He
dismissed previous plans, to have an electric truck towing the
balloon or an electric balloon towing the truck, and insisted on
having both balloon and truck free to move independently,
with a spring-loaded mechanism to lengthen or shorten the
extension lead as required, and to prevent it from hanging in
loops.

Diesel seems sometimes to have been rather optimistic in
his plans, for even if the truck had not run into a river or some
insurmountable obstacle in pursuit of the balloon, and even if
the cable had not snagged on a tree or a building, then the loss
of power in an enormously long trailing lead would almost
certainly have rendered the invention virtually useless!

A leading design or just a
basket case? Diesel's spring-
loaded mechanism for
'Improvements in Supplying
Electrical Energy to Electrically
Propelled Aerial Machines and
Balloons' (1897)

5 Perpetual motion?

*As soon as people began to make machines they must
have dreamed of machines that would work for nothing
– clever devices that would operate on their own,
grinding corn or pumping water from the well. By the
Middle Ages the hunt for* perpetuum mobile *had
become a kind of mechanics' quest, like the hunt for the
Holy Grail or the philosopher's stone that would turn
everything to gold – and just like those other quests this
one seemed to be impossible in practice.*

Imagine a heavy flywheel, perfectly balanced, that once set
spinning goes on and on. If there were no friction and no air
resistance, it would surely spin for ever – and that would be

perpetual motion. A more
useful flywheel would be
one that could spin with
such energy that it could
drive millwheels and still
spin for ever. This would
seem to be more difficult to
build, but could it perhaps
be achieved by some clever
arrangement of cogs, or
clever use of gravity?

The desire to invent a perpetual-
motion machine has certainly kept
inventors going round in circles

Magic wheels

Among the earliest and best-known designs was the wheel with curved spokes fitted with sliding weights, or with ball bearings that ran along the spokes in grooves. The idea is that, as each spoke passes the top, the weight runs to the outside, and as each spoke gets to the bottom the weight returns to the centre, so that there is always more weight on the right-hand side of the wheel, which therefore spins clockwise.

Not a wheel of fortune: the fallacy of perpetual motion (c. 1638)

This was probably the basic design of a famous engine built by Edward Somerset, the second Marquis of Worcester, who was a friend of Charles I (his father had been made a marquis after giving the King vast amounts of money). The Marquis had an exciting life: he fought in the Civil War, was banished in 1648 and spent four years in France, was captured when he came back to England, and was imprisoned in the Tower of London for two years until Cromwell let him out.

The Marquis's wheel, which he demonstrated to the King before the Civil War, in 1638 or 1639, was 14 feet in diameter and had 40 sliding weights of 50 pounds (23 kilos) each. As he explained in his book *Century of Inventions* (published in 1663 and dedicated to Charles II), it was built:

> To provide and make that all the Weights of the descending side of a Wheel shall be perpetually further from the Centre than those of the mounting side, and yet equal in number … A most incredible thing, if not seen, but tried before the late King (of blessed memory) in the Tower, by my directions, two

Extraordinary Embessadors accompanying His
Majesty, and the Duke of Richmond, and Duke
Hamilton, with most of the Court, attending Him.

He allegedly experimented with a version of this wheel
known as the 'water-commanding engine', also described as a
'hydraulic machine', on the walls of his home, Raglan Castle,
and it was said to be able to 'raise to the height of forty feet,
by the strength of one man and in the space of one minute of
time, four large buckets of water'. There is also a suggestion
that the same machine had the power of 'driving up water by
fire', and as a result some people have claimed that the
Marquis invented the steam engine! In 1663 Worcester
managed to get through an Act of Parliament which gave him
a monopoly of the profits from his machine. He promised to
pay 10 per cent to the King, and hoped to pay off his debts
with the rest. However, cynical Robert Hooke – who was
curator of experiments at the Royal Society, and who
formulated the famous Hooke's law (of elasticity) – described
his engine as 'one of the perpetual-motion fallacies'.

The Marquis was an enthusiastic inventor, however, and
was not likely to have been put off by a rude
comment from Robert Hooke. His 1661
patent, couched in the most curious
language, describes a variety of
improbable-sounding clocks, guns,
carriages and boats. The first of these
modest proposals was for a watch or
clock that would keep perfect time
without having to be wound up –
another impressive claim of perpetual
motion. Unfortunately, those early
patents were not provided with any
explanation or diagrams, so we have no

A wheel that
shall turn of
itself?

idea how he proposed to bring about the miracles he promised.

A clever variant of the Marquis's wheel was the wheel with hinged spokes, like elbows. As each spoke passed the top the weighted 'hand' would swing over, increasing the turning moment or torque, so that again the wheel should revolve clockwise. This idea is at least 600 years old, for Henry Dircks, writing about perpetual motion in 1861, gives an account of an invention by the early thirteenth century architect Wilars (or Villand) de Honnecourt, who said:

> **Many a time have skilful workmen tried to contrive a wheel that shall turn of itself; here is a way to do it by means of an uneven number of mallets ...**

Wind and water

Five hundred years ago, the Italian philosopher and alchemist Mark Anthony Zimara designed an elegant perpetual-motion system – a windmill whose output drove giant bellows in order to make wind to drive the windmill.

Then there were designs based on the flow of water or some other liquid – perhaps quicksilver, as mercury was called. The simplest plan was a cleverly shaped funnel; the greater weight of liquid in the wide part of the funnel was supposed to push the liquid through so that it ran right over the top and back into the funnel again – and on the way it could drive a water wheel, which would do useful

The perpetual-motion wind machine was not something to bellow about

work. Unfortunately what actually happens is that water reaches the same level in both sides of the vessel, regardless of the width of the tubes. The pressure depends only on the depth, not on the weight of water.

A perpetual-motion water system or a load of cog wash?

A more complex design would use the flow of water from a cistern to turn a water-wheel, use some of the energy from the water wheel to pump the water back up, and use the rest to do useful work; the English physician Robert Fludd described such an arrangement in 1618, using an Archimedes' screw to pump the water up, and grinding corn with the surplus energy. Alas, in real life the water wheel cannot supply enough energy to pump the water back up to the top.

An entirely different type of machine was described at length, and with full scientific detail, by the Swiss mathematician Johann Bernoulli. This depended on the fact that two different liquids may mix completely with one another and yet have quite different densities. He did not specify the liquids, but water and alcohol mix, and have different densities; so in principle the machine should run on brandy. The brandy is placed in a tall tank which contains a narrow vertical tube. At the bottom of the tube is a special filter that allows alcohol but not water to pass through – rather like the semipermeable membranes of cell walls, which allow water to pass through but not sugars.

When the tank was full, Bernoulli said, alcohol would flow through the filter and fill the narrow tube, and, because alcohol is less dense than water, the alcohol would fill the tube to a greater depth than the water. In fact the density of alcohol is only 0.8 grams per millilitre; so if the depth of the water were 20 centimetres the depth of the alcohol would be 25 centimetres – in other words the alcohol would rise 5 centimetres above the water. Therefore the narrow tube could be arranged so that the alcohol flowed out and back into the large container, driving a wheel on the way.

Sad to say, Bernoulli failed to explain just what filter will pass alcohol but not water …

Sir William Congreve – the man who designed rockets for the army in the early 1800s, burned Boulogne to the ground by mistake in 1806, and founded the Royal Artillery Rocket Brigade – invented in 1827 a perpetual-motion machine of some subtlety. An endless band of sponge is looped round a triangle of rollers, and is in turn surrounded by an endless heavy chain. The bottom side of the triangle dips into a reservoir of water, which soaks into the sponge by capillary action.

Without the heavy chain the water in the vertical and sloping sides would balance, but the heavy chain squashes all the water out of the sponge. This makes the vertical sponge (unsquashed) heavier, and so the sponge and the chain move round anticlockwise.

Or at least they should. But alas they don't.

Congreve's perpetual-motion machine (1827) – a nice idea but …

Magnetic motion

Alexander Bain, inventor of the fax machine, spent a good deal of time and money trying to make a perpetual-motion machine, probably using the newfangled techniques of electricity and magnetism, which must have seemed almost like magic. However, the idea was not new.

In his classic book *De magnete*, published in 1600, William Gilberd talked about making perpetual motion by using magnets, and he was a bright chap; the great Italian scientist Galileo said of Gilberd:

> I extremely praise, admire, and envy this author, for that a conception so stupendous should come into his mind...

and the poet John Dryden said:

> Gilberd shall live till lodestones cease to draw.

In 1648 the Bishop of Chester described a system in which a lodestone magnet would pull a steel ball up a slope:

> which steel as it ascends near to the lodestone may be contrived to fall through some hole in the plane, and so return to the place from whence at first it began to move; and being there the lodestone will again attract it upward till coming to the hole it will fall down again; and so the motion will be perpetual ...

The great Sir David Brewster, inventor of the kaleidoscope, was fooled in 1818 by a magnetically driven machine that apparently achieved perpetual motion. The sad thing is that none of these machines has worked, nor will any such machine.

The person who first began to think clearly about the

nature of energy and especially heat was James Prescott Joule, who worked in Salford in the 1840s and 1850s. He measured how much heat was generated when he used various machines to do work, and he concluded that energy can neither be created nor destroyed.

Joule said:

> The grand agents of Nature are by the Creator's fiat indestructible; whenever mechanical force is expended an exact equivalent of heat is always obtained ... It is manifestly absurd to suppose that the powers with which God has endowed matter can be destroyed any more than they can be created by man's agency.

In other words, though for somewhat unscientific reasons, James Prescott Joule was the first person to recognise the conservation of energy.

Joule's work led to the whole science of thermodynamics, whose laws were gradually sorted out in Scotland, France, Germany and England, during the second half of the nineteenth century. The laws of thermodynamics turn out to be universal and unbreakable; they are some of the most fundamental laws of nature, and there is no way round them. The First Law says that energy cannot be created or destroyed, which means that even if perpetual motion were possible – suppose a wheel could spin without any friction or air resistance, for example – no useful energy could be taken out of the system. In other words, the wheel could not do any work without slowing down.

This turns out to have a simple common-sense analogy. Suppose I were to go on my bike from the top of Ben Nevis to sea level at Fort William, five miles away. I would have descended 4,400 feet (1,340 metres) – which corresponds to the potential energy I have lost.

Now suppose I go the wrong way up the Great Glen, and from the top of Ben Nevis ride via Inverness, Aberdeen, Arbroath, Dundee and Perth to the sea at Fort William, I shall still have descended 4,400 feet, however many mountains and valleys I have crossed in between. So the change in height – or energy – is the same, regardless of the path I take.

And, if I go back to the top of Ben Nevis, I shall have climbed 4,400 feet, whichever way I go. Then, having completed a circuit, I shall have descended a total of zero feet, used zero potential energy in total. Whenever any system completes a cycle and gets back to where it started, the total energy change must be zero. And that means that no perpetual-motion machine, however it is built, can deliver energy and carry on going at the same speed, because when it gets back to where it started it must either have all its original energy, or have given some of it up and have less of its own. A simple way of stating the First Law is 'You can't win!'

In real life, there is always friction when any parts are moving. To overcome this friction takes energy, which is converted to heat. As a result, the machine must slow down, since its energy is being used up.

The Second Law of thermodynamics is even more brutal; 'You can't even break even!' Long before thermodynamics had been dreamed up, good scientists recognised that perpetual motion is impossible. Newton implied it in his great book *Principia*, published in 1687, and the Parisian Academy of Sciences refused in 1775 to accept any more perpetual-motion schemes. However, the lure of finding a magical source of energy remained irresistible. Even though the laws of thermodynamics were well understood by about 1900, they have not prevented people from going on trying to find ways round them.

The first British patent for a perpetual-motion machine was granted in 1635, and by 1903 there were 600 patents;

now the British Patent Office will not accept perpetual-motion applications. Every year the US Patent Office receives about a hundred patent applications for perpetual-motion machines, even though they insist on working models; they now send this response to those who submit such applications:

> The views of the Patent Office are in accord with those scientists who have investigated the subject and are to the effect that such devices are physical impossibilities. The position of the Office can only be rebutted by a working model. ... The Office hesitates to accept fees from applicants who believe they have discovered Perpetual Motion, and deems it only fair to give such applicants a word of warning that fees cannot be recovered after the case has been considered by the Examiner.

Even so, people are not discouraged. In his page on the World Wide Web, A.E. Wilcox writes:

> Most people discount perpetual motion devices, because they believe that ALL such devices break either the first or second law of thermodynamics. My device doesn't break either. It's what some might/should call a perpetual motion device of the third kind. Let me stress that just because all known perpetual motion devices have broken the first or second law, doesn't imply that all possible perpetual motion devices must break the first or second law.

Perpetual-motion machines are as impossible as the magic stone that turneth all to gold, but, if you want to try to make one, good luck!

6 Batty bicycles

The history of the bicycle is shrouded in mist, confusion and argument, which seems curious, since it is such a simple and useful form of transport. We actually know much more about early trains and aircraft than we do about early bicycles. His notebooks suggest that Leonardo da Vinci dreamed of a bicycle, and his dream is so close to the modern form that it is hard to believe that hundreds of years went by before the machine was actually built.

Horse-drawn carriages were used by the Romans, and by early Britons – Boudicca had one with knives on the wheels. Ox carts were routinely used for transport during the Middle Ages. There were tricycles in the eighteenth century: the Scottish engineer William Murdoch built himself a tricycle to

Bicycle from the notebooks of Leonardo da Vinci – although some experts believe this particular sketch was added centuries after Leonardo's death

go to school in Ayrshire in the 1760s, for example. Steam carriages came into use in the early 1800s, and by the 1830s railways were snaking across the country. How is it possible that no one had by then invented the bicycle, which is a far simpler machine?

Perhaps it would have been too expensive for the working man, and even more so for women, while the upper classes would have been appalled at the idea of having to propel themselves by their own efforts. Nevertheless, I am amazed that the first bicycle did not appear until 1839, and the bicycle as we know it not until the 1860s and later.

The invention of the bicycle

In 1817 Karl von Drais patented what came to be known as the hobby horse – a bench balanced on two wheels. You sat astride it and pushed along on the ground with your feet. This tended to wear out the shoe leather, and even the iron-soled shoes that were made, but nevertheless enjoyed a brief popularity in the 1820s, when everyone who was anyone had to have one.

The next giant leap forward had to be a leap in the imagination, to grasp the idea that it might be possible to balance on two wheels without keeping both feet on the ground! As far as we know, this idea was first put into practice in 1839 – in the shape of a wooden-framed machine with wooden wheels – by a Scottish blacksmith, Kirkpatrick MacMillan, at Courthill Smithy in the parish of Keir about 14 miles north of Dumfries. Kirkpatrick MacMillan was born in Keir in September 1812, and became a blacksmith like his dad. He probably went off to work in a foundry in Glasgow, returned to Keir, and took over the business when his dad retired in 1851.

Big wheels were good for rough ground and for speed

In the 1860s pedal-driven bicycles were made by Michaux in Paris; they were called boneshakers or velocipedes, depending on whether you were more impressed by their painfulness or their speed. The 'ordinary' – the high bicycle, or penny-farthing – came along about 1870. This was a sensible development. Drive to those early bikes was by pedals attached directly to the front wheel. There were no gears, and usually no brakes; you slowed down by back-pedalling.

Most of the people who took to the bicycle wanted to go fast, to get from A to B in a hurry, and to impress their friends, and the speed of a bicycle with direct drive depended directly on the size of the driving wheel. With a front wheel six feet across you could go three times as fast as with one two feet across.

There were considerable disadvantages to this. Getting on to a high bicycle is tricky. I know: I have done it. You need either a mounting block as used for getting on to a horse or a good deal of courage and skill to push forward, put one foot on the footrest low down, and then vault into the saddle as

A bicycle made for two (1869)

the bike moves off. Riding also is nerve-racking, since you are perched about six feet, or a couple of metres, off the ground, which feels extremely high.

Once going, the high bicycle is much more stable than a modern bike, because the huge front wheel gives you so much rotational inertia – it's like a great flywheel which once spinning is extremely hard to twist. So I am told you can ride with your hands off the handlebars at 2 m.p.h. However, if you hit a serious bump or pothole you go straight over the front wheel and land on your face from a great height. Many cyclists were injured this way.

And even getting off is an acquired skill. After slowing down by back-pedalling you ease out of the saddle, step back down on to the tiny footrest, allowing the bicycle to move away from under you, and then gently step down on to the ground – at least that is the theory.

Partly because it was so terrifying, and partly because it was so fast, the high bicycle was tremendously popular with the young men who were the most enthusiastic cyclists in the 1870s and 80s. Its demise started quite suddenly on 18 May 1889, when Willie Hume appeared for a race on the Queen's College playing fields in Belfast. Everyone laughed at him, for, while all the other riders had high bicycles, he was on a safety bicycle, with the silly pneumatic tyres recently constructed by the local vet, a certain John Boyd Dunlop. The spectators stopped laughing when Hume won the race, and suddenly everyone wanted the new tyres, and the high bicycle began to go out of fashion.

So that was how modern bicycles developed, but what about the MacMillan machine? It had a massive, heavy, wooden frame, reminiscent of the hobby horse, and wooden wheels like cartwheels, bound with iron tyres. The front wheel was steered with handlebars, more or less as on a modern bike. But the propulsion system looks distinctly odd to

modern eyes. There were cranks on the back wheel, and from
them treadles came forward to hang beside the front wheel.
You put your feet on the treadles, and propelled the bike by
pushing forward with alternate feet (instead of pushing down,
as on modern pedals). Pedalling it, sliding the feet to and fro,
reminded me of when my dancing partner tried to teach me
the tango ... And steering is tricky because the treadles
prevent the front wheel from turning more than about 20
degrees.

Apparently the original machine weighed half a
hundredweight (25 kilos), and MacMillan frequently rode the
14 miles into Dumfries in less than an hour – which is
impressive, to say the least. Critics say MacMillan's machine
was not the precursor of the modern bike. Drive to the back
wheels didn't come into serious use for another 40 years, and
the treadles were a blind alley.

What's more, there isn't much evidence that MacMillan
really built and rode such a machine – except an article in the
Glasgow Argus of 1842 which said that a gentleman of
Dumfriesshire had ridden 40 miles from Old Cumnock to
Glasgow – in five hours – and there, in a crowd of spectators,
had mounted the pavement and knocked over a small child.
Luckily the child was unhurt and the gentleman was fined only
five shillings (25 pence). Unfortunately the article does not
mention MacMillan by name – and he was not a gentleman –
nor does it say that the velocipede was a bicycle.

Superior saddles

Whether or not MacMillan's machine was a failed invention,
and whether or not it was the true precursor of the modern
bicycle, when the bicycle really arrived, in the 1880s, it
spawned a mass of new inventions, some for radical new
types of bicycle and some for outlandish accessories.

Probably the most common of these were for new saddle designs, which came in all shapes and sizes. Take for example the clever idea of Frederick William Barratt, ironmonger of Wimborne, who was probably worried about his wife's safety, and in 1899 patented a saddle 'of the ordinary or hygienic pattern but in the front centre of peak I introduce a wheel or roller of suitable material, grooved or otherwise. The object is to facilitate mounting and dismounting and to entirely obviate the danger caused by the dress catching. The wheel or roller … revolves as the rider gets on and off the saddle.'

He went on to explain:

It is well known that ladies attain or mount the saddle by an upward and backward spring movement, at the same time pressing forward with the foot upon one pedal. This action causes a considerable pressure upon the peak of saddle as the dress glides over same and it is not infrequent that in doing so with the ordinary saddle the dress catches with more or less risk of falling.

A further difficulty experienced by a large number of female cyclists is the fact that they are compelled to fix the saddle too low, owing to their inability to spring into the saddle when it is at its proper height in consequence of the friction of the ordinary peak, and suffer thereby from what is known as knee cramp. My invention entirely obviates the danger of the dress catching and greatly facilitates the mounting, doing away with these two objectionable features of the ordinary saddle.

Sadly, Mr Barratt's idea did not seem to catch on, and women's saddles still tend to be something of a problem, although nowadays women usually ride wearing trousers or cycling shorts, rather than voluminous dresses.

Some of these 'improved' saddle designs were rather

trivial, and reflected concern for the body's tender spots, or as one patentee put it 'the organic parts'; others were ludicrously complex, but for me they provide a sort of window into the Victorian mind. Here is a problem – a slightly irritating thing like an uncomfortable cycle saddle – so let's invent something to fix it. The Victorian age was the age of machines of all sorts, from steam carriages to aircraft, and the idea of a machine to solve each problem was firmly rooted in the fertile Victorian mind. It was also the age of the entrepreneur, and many of the inventors rushed to the Patent Office to protect their brainchildren. Just leafing through the old patents provides some fascinating insights.

George Augustus Youngman, manager of St Stephen's Cycle Works in Norwich, patented a new form of saddle by connecting the peak or fore-end with the underframe, 'as to more effectually distribute the stress on the leather or other flexible material from which the said seating is formed, and thereby to provide for the greater comfort of the rider'.

Joseph Fowler Steele and Harry Vaughan Currie, of the Albion Mills Saddlery Company in Birmingham, interposed under the leather upper 'a pad of stiffer leather and also a pad of felt or india-rubber, or like material, for the purpose of distributing the weight and of affording a more comfortable seat for the rider'. They also included 'a central supporting spring or supplementary elastic support of such resistance as to prevent undue or inconvenient deflection of the central part of the saddle seat, but to yield sufficiently under the motion of the cycle to absorb any jarring or like action'.

One of the most amazing inventions I have come across for the improvement of cycle saddles was a device dreamed up by a retired tea planter, Richard Wade Jenkins. He claimed this would also be able to maintain a constant level on ships at sea (reminiscent of Bessemer's boat – page 15). The basic idea was simple: a shallow watertight tank filled with water or other

A tricycle made for two (1883)

incompressible fluid was bolted to the saddle or other platform to be kept level, and supported on pistons which were free to slide up and down in cylinders; the pistons were fixed by hinges to the cycle frame or boat deck. However much the bicycle leaned or the ship rocked, he suggested, the water would retain its own level, and the saddle or platform, resting on the pistons, would therefore stay perfectly horizontal. He explained the mode of action thus:

> **It is obvious that as the under part or support rests on the swaying ship or the like, it partakes of all the motions and communicates them … to the plungers**

acting directly on the confined fluid. As the plunger rises, forced up by the rising deck, the pressure which it exerts upon the fluid supported above it, acts instantly through the incompressible water on the opposite falling piston, the mobile fluid thus forced from the one cylinder at once occupying exactly the same space in the opposite cylinder above the falling piston.

But insamuch as the falling piston, necessarily following the declining deck, would leave a vacuum, it is instantly followed by the fluid above it so that the opposite corresponding rising plunger, not only finds small resistance to overcome in lifting and following its superincumbent fluid, but is simultaneously urged to its work by the pressure of the atmosphere below it, thus providing the overpart with legs or supports lengthening and shortening in response to the rising and falling deck, leaving the horizontal position of the overpart unaffected.

He went on to outline how useful this horizontal platform would be for mounting light guns, searchlights, observation platforms for officers, deckchairs, seats, benches, berths, tables and the like.

There seem to me to be a number of flaws in Mr Jenkins's argument. To begin with, why did he want to keep his cycle saddle horizontal? The sensation would be rather disconcerting, and would make it difficult to keep contact with both pedals. However, this is a small drawback compared with the fact that it clearly would not work, since there is nothing in this design to keep the saddle or platform horizontal. Indeed I reckon the moment it tipped even slightly from the horizontal, it would overbalance completely, throwing the rider wildly off balance, and casting deckchairs, guns and observing officers into the sea!

Artful accessories

Richard Singer of Leipzig in the Kingdom of Saxony, perhaps still worrying about ladies' dresses, patented a brush for cleaning bicycle chains. The two halves of the brush are clamped on to the chain, which is then pulled through to remove all the mud, oil and grease that might otherwise stain the clothes.

Frank Mossberg of Attleborough, Massachusetts, produced a brilliant design for a bicycle bell in 1899. The bell was mounted on the front of the frame, just above the front wheel, and activated by a lever on the handlebars. This lever pulled a cord which pulled a coaster wheel on to the side of the front tyre – just as some dynamos are driven today. This wheel activated a pair of hammers which pounded alternately on the inside of the bell, so that it continued to ring as long as you pulled the cord and the front wheel was still turning.

Furthermore he introduced a cunning friction drive inside the bell in order to 'reduce the relative number of strokes on the bell as the speed of the bicycle is increased, as one great difficulty … is to make the ringing of the bell clear and not to have the strokes run into each other, and make a confused sound … With my improved friction motion … the number of strokes will be greatly equalised in fast or slow riding.' With or without the confused sound, I would love to have one of Mr Mossberg's bells on my bike!

The environmental demands were rather different in Sydney, in the Colony of New South

Singer's cycle-chain
cleaning brush (1897)

Wales, where John Howard used exactly the same sort of
drive system for a bike-powered sheep-shearing machine
'specially adapted for use by small sheep farmers who do not
require large installations of machine sheep shears or other
similar implements'. This was simple and clever:

> The bicycle may be ridden from shed to shed by one
> of the shearers, and when thus travelling, the stand E
> will be caused to assume the position shown by the
> dotted lines ... When it is desired to start work, the
> stand E is brought down to the position shown in the
> drawings, and secured by bolts or screws, to the floor
> of the shed, to a plank or other suitable base which
> may be handy. It will thus be seen that the driving
> wheel A of the bicycle will be raised from the ground
> and free to rotate without propelling the machine
> forward, while the friction pinion J being in close
> contact with the tyre, the power developed by the
> rider will be communicated to the axle H and thence
> to the sharpening disc K and the flexible shaft L at the
> outer end of which is the implement to which power is
> to be conveyed.

He was clearly an experienced engineer, and must have
tried and tested his apparatus, for he points out that 'The
sharpening disc K will have a double function. It will act as a
fly wheel and governor to regulate and equalise the driving
speed. With a view to the same end, the tyre B, instead of
being inflated with air, may be filled with water, thereby
adding to the weight and increasing its momentum without
increasing the speed at which it is driven.' I am not sure about
riding the bike with the back tyre full of water, but otherwise
this looks like an excellent piece of machinery; I almost wish I
had a sheep to try it out on!

Driving gear

Many patents were taken out for improved driving gear. William Francis Hackman of Uxbridge devised a system to transfer power from cranks to the driving wheel through the medium of coupling rods, housed within the backstays. Friedrich Fasterling of Prussia transmitted power from the pedals to the cranks by means of a link parallelogram; he claimed that 'by this means the pedal crank axle is driven very easily in all positions of the cranks'.

A watchmaker, Giovanni Antonio Philipon of Lima, Peru, came up with a novel design in which the cyclist pushed the pedals forward instead of downward 'by which I secure a more advantageous application of the muscular power, at the same time enabling the rider to keep his balance more easily.' Pushing forward with your feet is curiously similar to what

Fasterling's diagram showing transmission of power from the pedals to the cranks (1899)

A unicycle (1884)

you must do to ride the Kirkpatrick MacMillan machine (page 53), and also a modern recumbent cycle, in which you lie back with your feet out in front.

Having tried both of these, I don't believe the application of muscular power is advantageous, and on Philipon's machine you would be in grave danger of fouling the front wheel with your outside foot whenever you turned a corner. It has the additional disadvantage that the immediate drive from the pedal levers to the chainwheel is by slots pushing studs as they slide past them. This is crude, inefficient and bound to cause rapid wear.

Alfred Robert Jardine from Lanarkshire chose a different method to get 'greater leverage in the application of driving force and greater ease in the propulsion of the cycle'. His complex set of levers connecting the pedals to the chainwheel seem to me to be bound to provide more friction and no gain. Using an ordinary bike with gears, you can get more 'leverage' by changing to a lower gear, while if you want longer travel for your feet you can fit longer cranks, as long as they don't hit the ground. Therefore, providing extra levers cannot help. Furthermore, the bicycle as we know it is extraordinarily efficient; when properly lubricated and set up, 98 per cent of the effort is said to go into forward propulsion. I find it hard to believe that any additional ironmongery can improve this efficiency to any significant extent.

Anyone who rides a bicycle will know that going up and down hills is rather frustrating, because, although you can get up tremendous speed going down, you can rarely use all that speed to coast up the other side; so often you have to slow down at the bottom, and then you lose most of your momentum. But perhaps this would not be so if you could only store the kinetic energy instead of wasting it all as heat, which is what happens when you apply the brakes.

A gentleman from Upper Norwood, James Stack Lauder,

Jardine's 'Improved' bicycle (1899)

An uphill struggle: an interpretation of Lauder's brilliant oscillating-cylinder bike (1899)

noticed both this fact and that the bicycle is made from hollow metal tubes, and came up with a brilliant idea. Impractical, I think, but nevertheless brilliant.

Lauder suggested mounting a pair of oscillating cylinders, one each side of the front wheel. As you zoom downhill, switch these cylinders into action, so that they pull in air, compress it, and pump it into the hollow frame. On a level road you throw the cylinders out of gear, and use the bike as normal, but when you are faced with an uphill stretch you switch the cylinders into drive mode, and use the compressed air stored in the frame to help drive the front wheel and pull you up the hill.

An additional advantage of this system is that, when used to compress air, the cylinders act to slow the bicycle, 'checking the rapid descent of the machine, thus avoiding the necessity of the ordinary brake … It is also proposed to utilise the store of air … to inflate the tyres, and to operate a whistle or siren, thereby entirely dispensing with the ordinary pump and bell.'

John Browne of Stoke Newington came up with what might perhaps be classed as a wheelchair, although he seems to have been a little optimistic about the power and stamina of the fingers. He called his contraption a 'manumotive vehicle' and said that it would provide 'a motive mechanism easily manipulated and by which gas, electric, or oil engines may be dispensed with – the mechanism itself consisting solely of gearing arranged and constructed so as to be worked by hand with the greatest facility'.

Reading these patents a hundred years after they were written, I am fairly sure that some of the machines they describe – the bike-powered sheep shearer, for example – had been built, tried and improved before the patent was applied for. Others, such as this manumotive vehicle, were simply figments of the imagination. Mr Browne has sketched – although without any constructional details – an elegantly shaped car body, with front and back seats, and therefore designed to carry at least two people. Indeed it must carry two people, since the inadequate-looking tiller for steering can be operated only from the front seat, while the person in the back seat, who would seem to have an uncomfortable half-lying position, has to supply all the driving power by twiddling a small wheel in front of the chest, using only the thumb and first finger. I estimate that to drive such a vehicle up the slightest hill would need the full force of both hands, even without anyone in the front seat, which would be a bit dangerous, since from the driving seat you could not steer ...

Perhaps the most hopeful of the ingenious ideas I have come across for powering bicycles was dreamed up by a house decorator, William Bettis of West Ham; it's a 'wind motor, to assist the rider while travelling'. The notion is simple: he mounted a fan or small windmill on the front of the bike, so that, when he was pedalling along, the rush of air would turn the blades. These were arranged with gears to help turn the wheels, so that, in his words, 'when the rider mounts to go forward it sets the whole of the parts in motion, and the motor wheel is assisting the rider by its velocity and the rider is being partly propelled by the current of air that he is passing through.

Going backwards?
An intepretation of Bettis's wind-motor bicycle (1899)

Thus he is receiving great ease.'

I wish I could believe it! There is a hint of perpetual motion about this scheme. In practice I reckon that a big fan on the front would enormously increase your air resistance, and make it almost impossible to do more than about 12 m.p.h. But if it actually worked then presumably you would sail off into a headwind without pedalling, and if ever you encountered a tailwind you would be in danger of going backward!

Crazy constructions

Of all the bicycle patents I have seen, the prize for battiness must surely go to Paul Herrmann of Berlin, who designed a bicycle made entirely from pleated cane. The frame was to be made of cane – or at worst, of cane with a wooden core. The forks were to be built from cane, and because they have 'to resist a great tendency to bending … are constructed … in the form of a trellis framework … This construction provided with diagonal supports is best capable of supporting the strain to be put upon it.'

The handlebars 'are kept completely hollow, are consequently very elastic and do not convey shocks to the hands of the rider … The saddle is formed of woven cane in the form of basket work … [which] assures the elasticity of the same and renders the application of springs unnecessary. The wheel tyres are either twisted spirally of Spanish cane and provided with a woven covering in tubular form of split cane, or they are formed … of several canes with the said covering twisted round a strong hemp cord …' And he goes on to say that bicycles made like this would be cheaper, lighter, and more shock-absorbent than ordinary bicycles, and almost unbreakable!

And then there were the unicycles and the tricycles, which look wonderful in the pictures, although they have scarcely survived the test of time.

A really wooden idea: Herrmann's pleated cane cycle (1897)

7 Flushed with failure

Flushing lavatories have been around for thousands of years – in his wonderful palace at Knossos on Crete, King Minos had flush-out lavatories with earthenware pans and wooden seats, and that was about 2000 BC. The Romans brought flushing toilets to Britain – you can still see the remains of a communal lavatory in the fort at Housesteads on Hadrian's Wall. However, the natives seem to have ignored this efficient sanitation, and as soon as the Romans left they went back to using holes in the ground.

Ajax

The first serious attempt we know about to invent a self-contained water closet was made by Sir John Harington, of Kelston Hall, near Bath. He was born in 1560, became a godson of Elizabeth I, and later achieved a reputation as a wit and a ladies' man at court. In 1598 he produced a book about a new kind of loo. The standard Elizabethan slang word for a lavatory or a privy was a Jakes; Harington jokingly called his book *The Metamorphosis of Ajax*, meaning the transformation of a lavatory. His book is full of such dreadful puns. He compares himself and his lavatory to Archimedes and his revelation in the bath, and he concludes with a practical section, on 'how unsaverie places may be made sweet, noysome places be made wholesome, filthie places made cleanly'.

The instructions say:

In the Privie that annoys you, first cause a Cesterne
... to be placed either behind the seat, or in any place,
either in the roome, or above it, from whence the
water may by a small pype of lead of an inch
[diameter] be convayed under the seat in the hinder
part thereof (but quite out of sight) to which pype you
must have a Cocke or washer [i.e. tap] to yeeld water
with some pretie strength, when you would let it in.

Next make a vessell of an oval forme, as broad at

A mock-up of Harington's self-contained water closet, Ajax (c. 1598)

the bottome as at the top, ii foote deep, one foote
broad, xvi inches long, place this verie close to your
seate, like the pot of a close stool ... If water be
plentie, the oftener it is used and opened, the
sweeter; but if it be scant, once a day is inough, for
a need, though twentie persons should use it.

The caption for the exploded diagram he provided said,
'This is Don Ajax house of the new fashion, all in sunder,
that a workman may see what he hath to do.' The completed
version, with fish in the cistern, was captioned 'Here is the
same all put together that the workman may see if it be well.'

Ajax was meant to be left with six inches of water in the
pan. To flush it, you unlocked the 'shell', unscrewed the bolt,
and pulled it out to open the plug, which is at the bottom of
the same rod. (The lock was to prevent 'children and busie
folke' from wasting water.)

Sir John Harington was clearly an entertaining character,
and his book shows not only that he thought a good deal
about bodily functions in general and lavatories in particular,
but also that he was not afraid to be explicit about them in
writing. Most of this book would have been unprintable in
Victorian times, and some of it raises eyebrows today.

Such a witty linguist and elegant ladies' man seems an
unlikely candidate for engineer and plumber, but his servant
M. Combe was certainly an artist, since he drew the pictures
for the book, and probably a plumber too, for he wrote the
practical section. Perhaps Combe was the designer, working
to Harington's general brief.

Apparently Harington convinced the Queen, for she
allowed him to build an Ajax in her palace at Richmond,
with a copy of the book chained to the wall beside it – but as
far as we know this and his own were the only lavatories
built to Harington's design; so Ajax was literally a wash out.

Slop closets

One of my favourite stories of lavatorial disasters is that of
the grand communal-slop-closet experiment in Stafford in
1894. The automatic slop-water closet, or tipper closet, had
a self-acting tipper. All the used bathwater and washing-up
water in the house, and sometimes the rainwater off the
roof, went not down the drain but into this tipper tank.
When full, it overbalanced, and the soapy water rushed
down a pipe and flushed the lavatory, which could be some
distance away – for example in a privy out in the yard.

This was undoubtedly an economical and ecologically
sound system, if only for the water saving, and also a
tremendous advantage in the winter, for the privy did not
have to have its own water supply, so it could not freeze up
in cold weather. However, there was a snag: heavy rain
made the cast-iron tippers discharge every few minutes, and
their clanging all through the night could keep the whole
family awake.

The idea of the tipper gradually spread throughout the
world of sewage disposal. Roger George Salter took out a
patent in 1848 that included the idea of putting tippers at
intervals in sewers and drains so that water would collect
until the 'self-acting flushing apparatus' tipped, on which
'the liquid rushes out with great velocity and force'.

Slop closets were in the 1890s seriously suggested as the
best method of sanitation for households of the future. In
1894 Staffordshire County Council instructed George Reid,
the County Medical Officer, to set up a major experiment
to test their efficiency, because they wanted 'to abolish the
obnoxious privy-midden system … which then prevailed
throughout the town, which … seriously endangered the
public health'. So 59 houses, in two streets, were plumbed
with slop closets. The sewage was all received in a well, large
enough to contain a day's flow. From there at 7 o'clock

every morning it was pumped into precipitation tanks, where they tried various types of filter and precipitant, none of which seemed to work very well.

'As regards the sewage itself,' Mr Reid wrote in his report, 'it is of the foulest description, indeed it far exceeds in foulness any sewage the analysis of which I have seen. Of course, considering the fact that it is composed solely of the slopwater of cottages and the excreta and urine of the inhabitants, one would naturally assume it to be fouler than would be the case had the closets in use been ordinary water-closets with a clean water flush. No doubt to a very large extent this is explained by the fact that the population contributing to the flow was entirely an artisan one ...' Although I do not understand why Mr Reid should expect skilled workers to produce particularly foul sewage!

He concludes his report sadly:

> **If then the Council determine to adhere to their intention of establishing the slop-closet system, it will, in my opinion, be necessary to ... adopt a scheme of land filtration. The other alternative is to introduce ordinary water-closets in place of slop-closets ... There are other objections, not least of which is the tendency to rapid putrefaction ... That this has been the outcome of the experiments is disappointing, still it is better that the knowledge should have been acquired now, before any harm has been done...**

And so the communal slop closet generally faded from the scene, although a few were still in use in the 1980s, and children remember them because of the sudden spooky underground roar when the monsters flushed.

Valve closets

The first British patent for a water closet was taken out by a London watchmaker, Alexander Cumming, in 1775; his lavatory had a sliding valve underneath to let the sewage out. The problem with this was that it tended to get encrusted, and in winter to freeze up, especially if the closet was outside. Yorkshireman Joseph Bramah's splendid closet of 1778 overcame this problem by using a hinged valve.

Soon after this there appeared ingenious new closet ideas. Thomas Rowntree produced a portable water closet in 1789, and in 1792 John Ashley patented a self-acting water closet, 'which constantly keeps itself sweet and cleaner'. When the user stood up, an arrangement of wires and levers let the sewage out of the pan and then opened valves to flush the closet automatically. Thomas Binns's self-acting closet of 1793 was even more cunning. When you sat down the seat sank about a quarter of an inch, which was enough to activate a crank and a wire, and allow the 'measurer' to fill from the main cistern. When you stood up again the valve from the cistern was closed, and that below the measurer was opened, so that the water from the measurer flushed the lavatory. Binns was clearly an enterprising fellow, for he also invented various portable water closets.

In 1796 William Law patented a closet in which he claimed 'Many Mechanical Gentlemen asert there are several Improvements ... that have not been produced before ... This Water Closet is principally intended to act by Riseing from the seat but may be acted by the handle ...' Gradually the lavatories became more and more sophisticated; most of them seemed to have exotic refinements that have not stood the test of time.

In 1821 Stephen Hawkins produced a valve closet with a cunning air trap, designed to eliminate smells. When you used it, the weight of sewage falling on the trap *a* overcame the counterweight *c*, so that all the stuff fell through, and then the trap *a* closed again, and no smell could escape – at least in theory!

Before about 1850 only those people rich enough to have their own water supplies and cesspits were able to have water

Hawkins's proposal for a sweeter-smelling water closet (1821)

closets, but during the 1850s and 1860s piped water and sewers gradually reached most of the houses in Britain, and with these connections came the possibility of domestic water closets for the middle classes. Here was a market opportunity not to be missed, and sure enough inventors queued for patents and vied with one another for the ingenuity of their systems.

By 1850 some 50 patents had been issued; by the end of 1855 there were more than a hundred, and after that the flood became a torrent. Many of these patents were for minor improvements in the flushing arrangements – Hans von Hosstrup, for example, invented 'a lever flushing-cistern in which an immediate flush is obtained by the pulling of the chain and an after flush is produced by the action of a

Hosstrup's double-flush cistern

syphon'; and Carl Nuber from Baden-Baden went to enormous lengths to make a powerful yet noiseless flushing system – but the fact is they were all failures, in that today's lavatories display little of the complex machinery that the Victorians were so fond of.

Crapper's ornamental flush-down W.C. (c. 1880)

The urinette

Women have always been badly provided with public lavatories; even today in any public building there are almost always more loos for men than for women, even though women necessarily take longer for each visit. There used also to be the unfair fact that going into a cubicle cost a penny; hence the term spending a penny.

In 1927, concerned that women always had to pay to use a cubicle, while men could use urinals without charge, the Public Health Committee in London reported that 'a fitment for women has been designed, known as a urinette. It is similar to a w.c., but is narrower and has a flushing rim … Urinettes are fixed in w.c. compartments, usually with a curtain in front instead of a door.'

The idea was that, if a woman wanted only to wee, she could use the urinette for free, with modesty provided by a curtain; it was like a urinal for women.

Eight boroughs installed urinettes in a total of 30 places, but, the report confesses, 'The urinettes are not popular … the attendants state that they are sometimes used in an uncleanly manner and require supervision to maintain them in a hygienic condition.' And now, as far as I know, there are no urinettes to be found, although the idea was reinvented in 1999.

However, there was one great invention that failed undeservedly, in my view: the earth closet.

Earth closets

Before the advent of water closets, primitive lavatories were just holes in the ground. Dig out a pile of earth, go in the hole, and then shovel on a little earth to cover the offering. Earth closets became more advanced with the patent of Thomas Swinburne in 1838: he arranged a separate urinal for collecting urine, and a reservoir containing ashes, so that a small amount could be released after each use of the closet. In 1860 the Rev. Henry Moule entered the fray, patented his own closet, started the Moule Patent Earth Closet Company, and sold a range of models, the expensive ones made of oak or mahogany.

Basically the Moule system was to bring in earth from the garden, dry it in a metal box under the kitchen range and put it in a hopper at the back of the wooden closet, which was used indoors. After using it, you pulled a handle to 'flush' it with dry earth from the hopper; the earth covered your production, and according to Moule rapidly removed the smell. The earth could be redried and reused several times, and Moule claimed that he had no smells in the house, but a luxuriant growth of vegetables in his garden.

In 1861 he produced a 20-page pamphlet entitled *National health and wealth, instead of the disease, nuisance, expense, and waste, caused by cess-pools and water-drainage*. 'The cess-pool and privy vault are simply an unnatural abomination,' he thundered, 'the water-closet ... has only increased those evils.' The main environmental arguments are simple: first, every time you use a water closet you throw away up to 2 gallons (10 litres) of expensive drinking water; secondly you are also throwing away useful fertiliser; and thirdly the sewage has to decompose somewhere; underwater decomposition is slow and anaerobic, which means that it produces unpleasant smells and encourages potentially dangerous bacterial growth. Decomposition in dry earth, however, is aerobic and rapid; the sewage is quickly converted to harmless compost, and there is minimal smell.

Moule quoted a biblical precedent for his efforts, from a set of instructions about cleanliness: 'And thou shalt have a paddle upon thy weapon; and it shall be, when thou wilt

Swinburne's earth closet
(1838)

ease thyself abroad, thou shalt dig therewith, and shalt turn back and cover that which cometh from thee.' (Deut. 23:13.) The New English Bible is even clearer: 'With your equipment you will have a trowel, and when you squat outside, you shall scrape a hole with it and then turn and cover your excrement.'

Henry Moule died in 1880, but even in his seventies he was still trying to persuade the government that the earth closet was the system of the future, and he managed to convince a lot of people. *The Lancet* of 1 August 1868 reported that 148 Moule dry-earth closets were used at the volunteer encampment at Wimbledon – forty or fifty of them daily by not fewer than 2,000 men – without the slightest annoyance to sight or smell. *The Field* of 21 November 1868, said 'In towns or villages not exceeding 2000 or 3000, we believe the earth-closet will be found not only more effective, but far more economical, than water drainage.'

Designs from Moule's Earth closet
catalogue (1870)

This combination of economy and health was powerful.
In 1865 the Dorset County School at Dorchester, with 83
boys, changed from water closets to earth closets, and cut
the annual maintenance costs from £3 to 10 shillings (50
pence)! At the same time smells and diarrhoea were
eliminated. Lancaster Grammar School brought in earth

closets because the water closets were always out of order 'by reason of marbles, Latin grammar covers, and other properties being thrown down them'.

For some decades in the second half of the nineteenth century, therefore, the earth closet and the water closet were in hot competition. Almost everything Moule said was true, and much the same arguments are used today by the champions of bioloos and composting lavatories; surely they represent our best hope for the future. The environmental considerations have not changed: using water closets is expensive, and merely shifts the problem downstream; the sewage has to decompose somewhere. Nevertheless in rich countries, because it does rapidly and effortlessly remove the sewage from the house, the water closet has won – so far.

Animal hygiene

An American book claims that any cat can be trained in 14 days to use an ordinary lavatory, and there have been many attempts to set aside special corners of parks for dog loos, mostly without conspicuous success, but two stories really caught my eye. An 1880 automatic stable was designed to allow horses and cows to walk on treadmills, and so do useful work, while at the same time collecting their own droppings, which could then be used directly as fertiliser.

I have not seen many of these automatic stables in use, but perhaps they will in any case be superseded by the Friendly Animal Trainer (FAT) recently developed by the Swiss Federal Station for Agricultural Economics and Engineering near Zürich. When a cow lifts its tail – as they do before performing – sensors warn the FAT, which lowers a pneumatically powered stirrup over the cow's neck and guides it to a 'toilet grill'. The sewage falls through on to a conveyor belt, and is taken away to generate methane, which

An automatic stable: enough to make a horse turn tail (1880)

heats the building. Meanwhile the rest of the floor stays clean.

Its inventor, Matthias Schick, claims that adult cows learn to use the machine in three weeks, but 'with young cows the process goes much faster. And you do not need to leave the trainer on all the time. You can use it one day and take it off the next.'

8 Domestic difficulties

The Victorian age of sophistication brought with it a number of obsessions, among which was the idea of constantly improving both yourself and your household. Somewhere near the heart of their worries lay the dreadful problem of personal hygiene.

Keeping clean

A Scarborough ironmonger, Alfred Wrightson, invented a cunning wire soap holder that would hang over the edge of the bath – or a pail or bowl – to hold the soap out of the water.

Edmund Roenius of Grand Rapids in Michigan was

Wrightson's 'Improved Soap Holder' (1899)

more ambitious with his soap hanger: he wanted to make sure the soap could not fall to the ground or be carried away. The cake of soap was moulded round a metal tube so that it could not be removed. It was then suspended on a chain which passed over a pulley on a bracket, and had a counterweight at the other end. The soap hanger was mounted on the wall. 'The soap is thus prevented from collecting dirt through contact with a soap dish, washstand, or other supporting surface, and it cannot slip from the hands of the user and fall on the floor. The device also effects a saving of soap and prevents the same from being lost or carried away.'

Bozérian's portable and collapsible shower bath (1880)

In 1880 Gaston Bozérian devised a handy portable and collapsible shower bath, in which the water was pumped up by hand to a small overhead reservoir. In 1897 the Parisians attending the Bicycle Exhibition were amazed to see the *Vélo-douche*, or bicycle shower. They suggested that the user could keep in training while washing, and one great advantage of the system was that, the harder you pedalled, the more powerful was the flow of water. A heater below the water tank would allow you to have a hot shower. Confident predictions were made that these *Vélo-douches* would become commonplace in cycling clubs and schools. In both these showers, the water seems to have been recycled; so it must have become gradually fairly soapy and grubby.

... and keeping fit

During the early eighteenth century, the Guppy family were a significant force in Bristol society. Thomas Guppy was an iron founder, and more than that a merchant venturer. He it was who invited Isambard Kingdom Brunel, impressed by his designs for the Clifton Suspension Bridge, to think about building a railway from Bristol to London (not from London to Bristol!). Tom Guppy became a close associate and even friend of Brunel, and worked with him on many projects. After a tremendous lunch at Taplow to celebrate the opening of the Great Western Railway, he walked along the top of the moving train as it steamed back towards Paddington, and twenty years later he cast the vital iron pipes for Brunel's ill-fated atmospheric railway.

Tom's brother Samuel Guppy was a successful merchant in Bristol, with posh premises in Queens' Square; he took out patents for improvements in the manufacture of nails and soap. Sam's wife Sarah Guppy must have been intrigued by these patents, and decided that she should also take out some of her own. In 1831 she patented an ingenious bedstead with special steps which slid under each side to prevent dust from gathering under the bed, as well as making it easier to get into and out of the bed. The bed was also fitted with 'a set of springs and rollers to be used for exercise when in bed'. In other words her bed made it possible to do pull-ups without even getting up first!

Kitchen capers

However, my favourite Sarah Guppy patent was taken out in 1812, for 'Certain improvements in tea and coffee urns'. She says she made her tea urn in any of the 'usual forms and constructions', but it had two clever modifications, in order to allow the user to make the whole of breakfast in one operation, instead of having to mess about with several different pieces of equipment. First she suspended an egg basket from the lid, so that the eggs in the basket hung in the water, and were boiled while the water was boiling to make the tea. And second, in the lid of the urn, she made 'an elegant and convenient support for a plate or dish or other vessel to contain toast or other article of food or refreshment' – in other words, a place to keep the toast warm. Why every modern kitchen is not equipped with one of Sarah's tea urns must remain a mystery.

Egg-boiling equipment has always been a favourite goal for inventors, and one of the more splendid examples of the genre was the automatic egg boiler patented by Dr Thomas Gaddes, a dentist in

Gaddes's automatic egg boiler (1897)

Harrogate. Actually there was not much automatic about the boiling process, but he devised a cunning way of snatching the egg from the boiling water at the right moment. Perhaps he was kept so busy by agonised patients demanding to have their teeth treated that he was unable to time his egg with a watch or even an hourglass egg timer, or perhaps he was just absent-minded, and wandered off, allowing his eggs to become hard as rocks.

The Gaddes machine depended on water dripping from

D'Oyly Grange's knife and razor stand (1899)

a reservoir, which therefore gradually became lighter and allowed the balance arm to tilt. This would have lifted the egg slowly from the water, but Gaddes realised that this might have left the egg hard underneath and soft on top, so he added a clever refinement in the shape of a fishing weight on a separate wire slide. As soon as this slide dipped below the horizontal, the weight slid to the other end of the wire, the balance of the arm was suddenly shifted and the egg was yanked from the water. The wire slide could be adjusted for large, medium or small eggs, and there was even a modification to allow two eggs to be boiled at the same time.

Harrogate must have been a town of ingenious chefs, for William D'Oyly Grange of Clarence Drive patented a special stand for holding knives and razors, in order to keep them sharp by means of a magnetic field. The knife or razor was placed in a box with the edge down and the whole of the blade at an angle of 15 degrees to the horizontal. Attached to the box was a compass to permit the box 'being placed in a particular position in relation to the magnetic field of the earth. At one end of the box ... is placed a weak magnet or as an alternative the compass. If a magnet it is to

Krogh's milk boiler (1899)

be removable. In using this appliance I take the magnet out and place the empty case or stand in a drawer or on a wooden shelf or other suitable place and turn the box until the north end of the needle points to an arrow on the stand or box.' He says that the knife or razor should always be left in a north–south line, in order to keep the edge sharp!

Marius Frederik Krogh developed a complex-looking piece of apparatus to prevent milk boiling over. When you put this into the saucepan the whole device sank directly on

Kürten's candle stove (1899)

to the level of the milk and, 'yielding gradually to the pressure of the boiling milk, prevented the boiling over of the latter ...' If the milk boiled too soon, it went up through the central funnel, spilled over, cooling, and ran back down through the perforations into the body of the liquid. 'The action of this apparatus is found to be excellent, one of the principal features being that the device can rise and fall ... according to as the milk boils more or less.'

Heated flower stand (1899)

Hubert Caspar Kürten of Switzerland invented a clever little clip to fit on a candle so that it could be used for cooking. The saucepan could have a flat bottom or a concave bottom (for more efficient heat transfer), and the three legs of the stand hung on the candle so that it descended as the candle burned. The saucepan remained at the same height above the flame. This looks as though it would be useful for making a cup of tea, although candle flames are rather sooty, as I remember from trying to use them for illegal toast production at school.

On the other hand, Marie Deutschmann's invention of a heated flower stand seems absurd. She says its object is to improve and accelerate the growth of the flowers placed inside it, but it seems to me that the heat from the spirit lamp she suggests would be enough to cook them!

From the cradle to the grave

Another great preoccupation of the Victorians was cradle rocking. Some parents – or perhaps nurses – seem to have thought that no baby could possibly get to sleep without being rocked in its cradle, and no doubt the gentle motion had a soporific effect. As a lad in the early 1800s Thomas Edmondson, who in later life made a small fortune from his brilliant idea of the locally printed railway ticket, complete with number and date stamp, built a combined cradle rocker and butter churn, so that anyone who was churning the butter would simultaneously rock the baby.

This sounds quite tough to me – churning the butter must be hard enough already, without having to rock the baby as well. What's more, I should have thought that butter churning must involve movements that are much quicker and more violent than would be ideal for baby rocking ...

However, this did not prevent the same idea being reinvented in America in 1873. I guess a man claimed credit for this invention, for he suggested it would employ 'the

A cradle-rocking machine (1873)

hitherto wasted female power' to rock the baby and make
the butter. 'By this means,' he went on, 'the hands of the
fair operator are left free for darning stockings, sewing, or
other light work ... Fathers of large families of girls ... are
thus afforded an effective method of diverting the latent
feminine energy, usually manifested in the pursuit of
novels, beaux, embroidery, opera-boxes, and bonnets, into
channels of useful and profitable labour.' He even suggests
that the device could 'supply power for washing-machines,
wringers, and other articles of household use'. This man
would not be popular if he made such suggestions today –
indeed I don't expect he was popular with women in 1873!

I am sure that many other cradle rockers were invented,

but one that was actually patented in 1899 by a Canadian called Lewis Cutten of the County of Turtle Mountain, was constructed rather like a grandfather clock: wind up the clock spring and let go. The cradle is driven one way by the spring, and then swings back under gravity, before being pushed again. All you need to try it out is an old grandfather clock and a baby!

One of the more flamboyant characters of the Industrial Revolution was John 'Iron-mad' Wilkinson, who was born on a market cart headed for Workington Fair, became an ironmaster in the West Midlands, and wanted to make everything from iron. He built an iron boat, which everyone else wrongly predicted would sink. He built an iron church, with iron pews and iron pulpit, now carefully painted to look like wood. He was involved in 1779 in the casting of the famous iron bridge, which spans the Severn and gave its name to the developing town there. And he cast himself an iron coffin, which he stood in the corner of his office and showed off proudly to all his visitors.

When he died in 1808 his body was placed in a wooden coffin and taken to the planned burial site at Castle Head, but unfortunately the wooden coffin was too big to fit into his iron coffin; so they buried him temporarily in the garden while a new coffin was cast. Then they dug him up, put the wooden coffin in the new iron coffin, and found that it was now too big for the hole in the rock. So they buried him temporarily again, blasted a bigger hole in the rock, and dug him up and buried him properly, with a huge iron obelisk above him. However, 20 years later the house changed hands, and the new owners objected to having this iron obelisk outside their windows; so poor Iron-mad was dug up for the third time and buried for the fourth time, at Lindale church.

A final twist: he had been so popular with his workers

that, seven years after his death, several thousand of them gathered on Monmore Green and sang for him, hoping that he would reappear on his grey horse, and lead them back to prosperity after the misery of the Napoleonic Wars. But it was all in vain – he stayed in his iron coffin.

Matches and sticks

One small difficulty that has beset people for a long time is that it takes two hands to light a match, which means that you lack a hand to hold the candle, lamp, cigar or whatever it is you need to light. I once met a pipe-smoking Jaguar driver, who after years of practice had perfected a way of taking a Swan Vesta from the box and striking it with one hand, so that he could light his pipe with one hand on the wheel. I greatly admired his prestidigitatory skill, but never mustered the time, patience and dexterity needed to do it for myself.

An elegant solution to the two-hand-match problem came from George Frederick Lawrence and Arthur Josiah Field, whose object was 'to produce a holder or box from which a match can be taken and through which when passing it can be automatically lighted, and held still burning for igniting a cycle lamp, pipe, cigar, or other article'.

Their claim continues: 'We make our holder in the form of a metal case in which we place a slide … having at one end flexible springing jaws on which are attached roughened or serrated lips for the match to pass through and be ignited. We arrange a pusher … for the purpose of ejecting the match … and for forcing it through the igniting jaws.' So the match was pushed between the sandpapery jaws and ignited as it emerged. They also allowed for it to be flipped through with a spring when released by a trigger, which

Delostal's illuminating idea: the electric match (1893)

would have been dramatic. In either case the device must have made it easy to light a match with one hand.

A hi-tech version of automatic ignition was provided in France by Monsieur Delostal; it looked like a bell and was called the electric match. The match is the stick in the middle, A, and has at its further end a hollow perforated space filled with cotton. When inserted into the bell this cotton soaks up flammable liquid from the reservoir E at the bottom, which is filled with felt saturated with a mixture of alcohol and ether. The instrument is connected to an electric battery by means of two wires. As the stick A is pulled out, it breaks an electrical contact with the small watch spring D. This causes an electric spark, which ignites the end of the match. *Eh voilà*; *le feu!* After use, the match is replaced in the bell, and the absence of air inside extinguishes the flame. *C'est magnifique, n'est-ce pas?*

The modern corollary to these autostrike matches is threefold. First we have gas or petrol lighters, which need only one hand. Second we have flint or electronic spark generators to light gas rings – rather as Monsieur Delostal had – and most gas cookers and central-heating boilers are fitted with automatic spark lighting, so that the gas cannot be turned on and left running. Third, many of us still use the simple match, as invented by John Walker in 1826.

Joseph Emmett was perhaps concerned about the number of cases of walking-stick-user's wrist in the community of East Dulwich when he patented his improved rubber-tipped ferrule for walking sticks, umbrellas, billiard cues and the like. He provided a metallic ferrule or collar, preferably conical, with both ends open, and placed a plug of indiarubber in the bottom, sticking out through the bottom of the cone. The other end fitted on the walking stick or umbrella, and was attached in the usual way. Emmett claimed that:

> **By this invention, the objectionable noise & concussion of the ordinary solid-tipped ferrule is entirely done away with; as likewise is the very sensible shock to the hand & arm felt at every impact between the ordinary solid-tipped ferrule & the hard pavement or road. The comfort of the user is largely increased by the interposition of the soft and yielding material especially in the case of aged and infirm persons.**

Domestic animals

William H. Wellstead, a farmer from Michigan, invented a clever system for feeding cows, which aimed 'to regulate the supply of feed to an animal so as to prevent too rapid eating, insufficient mastication, and waste of feed'. The feeding trough could move vertically up and down, and was supported by an adjustable weighted lever, so that when the cow pressed with its nose on the trough a limited amount of grain or other feed would fall into the trough, and when the pressure of the nose was removed, the flow of grain stopped.

He claimed that:

> **The animal is thus prevented from eating too rapidly and is compelled to masticate and digest its feed more thoroughly, thereby enabling it to assimilate a larger percentage of its feed and to be kept in a better and healthier condition with less feed than when the usual methods and appliances are employed. The waste that occurs from scattering, slobbering or moistening with saliva what is not eaten, when a considerable quantity of grain or feed is given to the animal at once, in the usual way of feeding, is prevented, and the disorders of the alimentary canal resulting from improper eating are also avoided.**

This limited supply of food seems quite sensible, although why it should force the animal to chew more thoroughly is not clear. I wonder whether the continued use of such a device would in time produce a race of supercows which would pick up a brick and dump it in the trough in order to release all the feed in the hopper!

Partly for the benefit of the horse, because the work would be easier, Giuseppe Vicenzo de Luca took out a

Collapsible bird cage (1879)

patent for a new lightweight plough, intended to be used in market gardens. The main innovation was a revolving ploughshare, which he asserted would be just the thing for the cultivation of light soils.

March 1879 saw the dawning of a new age in New York bird care, for Owen W. Taft received a patent for a collapsible bird cage, or as he put it 'a bird cage adapted primarily to being taken to pieces and packed in smaller compass for facility of transportation, and constructed so that it is held in its complete integral form by a tension exerted either individually or collectively upon the several wires constituting the same'.

I assume the point of having a collapsible bird cage was that it was easy to take to the country for the weekend, or to Long Island for a vacation, but what Mr Taft fails to explain in his long and complex patent is what you were supposed to do with the poor inhabitant when the cage was collapsed. Did you have to have a collapsible bird as well?

9 Medical marvels

People have always disliked being ill, and much human time and energy have been devoted to gadgets and tinctures intended to improve the sense of well being; that is to make people who are ill – or think they are ill – feel better. There must have been many more remedies proposed than there are diseases to treat, from the proverbial snake oil of the charlatan pedlars of the Wild West to the soothsayer's charms that were supposed to dispose of warts. Here are just a few of the more bizarre ideas.

Pneumatic medicine

During the seventeenth and eighteenth centuries, 'taking the waters' was a fashionable way for people who felt generally unwell to treat themselves, and one of the popular resorts was Hotwells Spa at Bristol, where hot murky water gushed out from St Vincent's Rock, roughly underneath where the Clifton Suspension Bridge now stands. Catherine of Braganza visited Hotwells in 1677, and that really put the

6 Dowry Square, home to pneumatic 'specialist' Dr Thomas Beddoes

Not all for laughs: Davy's trick of inhaling nitrous oxide became a great success with medics (1799)

place on the map. Many of the people who came lodged down the road in elegant Dowry Square, and at No. 6 Dr Thomas Beddoes set up in October 1798 his brand-new Pneumatic Institution, hoping to cash in on all these sick visitors. As medical superintendent he hired the 19-year-old Humphry Davy.

The Pneumatic Institution was funded by private subscription – they had £1,500 from the potter Josiah Wedgwood, for example – and its aim was to find out whether the various gases that had recently been discovered by Priestley, Lavoisier and others had any useful medicinal value. The institution took eight inpatients and up to 80 outpatients, many of whom had tuberculosis, which was common at the time, and deadly. Because tuberculosis clearly affected the breathing system, Beddoes hoped that some form of gas therapy would be effective; he and Davy tried all sorts of gases.

Beddoes apparently believed that cows were healthy beasts, and therefore that patients with tuberculosis might be cured by the gases produced by cows. As far as we know he did not actually take cows into the ward, but he kept a small herd in the garden next door, and piped the gases into the bedchambers. These gases, you understand, were what the cows breathed out, and what came from the other end as well … There is no evidence that this weird treatment did the patients any good at all, but I imagine there was quite an incentive to feel better and discharge yourself!

However, this curious obsession with gases did have one useful side effect, for Davy discovered the wonderful effects of inhaling nitrous oxide, which came to be called laughing gas. He used to wander round the Downs, breathing it from a green silk bag, and he introduced the practice to his friends. The poet Robert Southey wrote to his brother, 'O Tom! Such gas has Davy discovered … it made me laugh and tingle in every toe and fingertip. Davy has actually invented a new pleasure for which language has no name!'

Today, nitrous oxide is used not so much by poets as by dentists, nurses and paramedics, for it is one of the most safe and useful of the anaesthetics; but it all started with Beddoes's theory about cows!

In 1876 Dr Carlo Forlianini opened an elegant Pneumatic Health Institute in Milan. The patient was taken into a cylindrical, comfortably furnished room (see below)

Portable
Turkish bath
(1899)

into which chemically purified air was blown at high pressure, using a steam engine. Dr Forlianini's theory was that the extra pressure forced the clean air into the tiniest tubules in the lungs, which improved the oxygenation of the blood, swept away any particles or impurities and strengthened the breathing muscles, bringing great benefits to those suffering from diseases of the blood, pulmonary or glandular systems.

The Turkish bath was all the rage in the late nineteenth century, but some people worried that, although the hot air was clearly beneficial to the skin and the body in general, it might perhaps be injurious to the lungs. So in 1873 the *British Medical Journal* announced to the world a new, improved, portable Turkish bath, which was designed to fit closely around the body, leaving the head free in order to spare the lungs. This apparatus was adjustable in every way,

The Quaker bath

and even had an attached cistern to provide the patient with a warm or cool shower, either slowly or rapidly. I am intrigued by the fact that this was clearly perceived as a medical treatment, and suggested by the *British Medical Journal* for the use of patients, whereas today Turkish baths are generally thought of as recreational.

A London mining agent, Arthur Lewis Pointing, patented an improved folding cabinet for vapour and hot-air baths, which was cheap and simple and so brought the portable Turkish bath within the range of ordinary people. Imagine a box about four feet (1.2 metres) in each dimension, the walls and lid being made of waterproof fabric on wooden frames. You sit inside this box on a chair, with your head poking out through a little hole in the roof, fitted with its own box, which can be thrown back to allow the user to breathe cool air. However, I believe the point was to fill the entire cabinet with steam, hot air or balsamic vapours, to ease the breathing system. And the beauty of the cabinet was that it would fold completely flat for easy storage!

Inhaler and Nasal douche (1899)

A popular American accessory was the Quaker steam or vapour bath, which was a cylinder of fabric, and cost only $5 by mail order. Steam for these portable baths could be provided from the kitchen kettle, or from a metal bowl of water into which was put a brick heated in the fire. Hot air was provided by a small spirit lamp.

Inhalation of beneficial vapours was widely used to treat

Taking the air or putting the kettle on? A home-made inhaler (1894)

all sorts of illnesses, real or imagined, and dozens of devices were dreamed up to assist in the process. James Monroe Munyon from Philadelphia patented a simple but ingenious combined inhaler and nasal douche. Either the vapour from medicament contained within the small vessel D could simply be inhaled through the mouthpiece, or the nosepiece K could be fitted, and the patient could blow into the mouthpiece to squirt the vapour up his nose – although blowing out through the mouth and breathing in through the nose might be a bit tricky.

Some patients have always believed in do-it-yourself medicine, as shown by the home-made inhalation equipment of 1894 (above).

A Manchester printer-turned-doctor, Charles Blackley, suffered dreadfully from hay fever, and was prompted to investigate what caused it in the spring of 1859, when his children brought some grasses into the house and set off the familiar symptoms much earlier than June, when he expected them. Some people said hay fever was caused by the smell of roses, others by dust, paint or varnish fumes, or even sunlight. He tried all these things on himself, and found that the only substance that caused real runny-eyed, snotty-nosed, phlegm-chested hay fever was pollen from grasses and flowers.

Charles Blackley never got as far as finding a cure for hay fever, but he suggested various ways of avoiding it, including muslin nose plugs to filter out the pollen. Unfortunately they proved awkward to use, and made breathing difficult, and they never caught on.

A Hungarian glass painter, Carl Kusché, invented an improved spittoon 'having a floating surface to receive the expectoration, said surface being capable of being depressed by the foot below the level of the water or other disinfected liquid in which it floats, and thus to wash off the impurities from the same'.

Encouraged perhaps by the acute hearing of elephants, Shamrao Babajee Powar of Bombay patented a neat piece of apparatus to assist hearing (overleaf). It comprised a pair of bent or hollowed plates of aluminium or celluloid, rather like convoluted sea shells. These fitted over and around the ears, leaving openings in front which had an area greater than that of the ears, thus forming a chamber to receive the sound waves on its inner surface and reflect them into the ear cavity. These plates could be held in place either by a light spring frame fitting over the top of the head, or by being attached to a handle held below the chin.

I am reminded of the Rev. John Blackburn of Sheffield,

who was worried that some of his congregation might not be able to hear the golden words of his sermons; so he constructed a parabolic reflector above and behind his pulpit in order to project his message more effectively into the church. History does not relate

Powar's Improved Hearing Device (1899)

whether this worked, but I am a bit worried that, if his reflector was truly parabolic, his thundering tones would all either go forth in a narrow parallel beam, or else, even worse, be focused on a single pew some distance in front of him, in which case one loyal churchgoer might be deafened, while all the rest of the congregation would be worse off than before!

Henry Tansley, gentleman of Brighton, was unhappy about conventional spectacle frames (see right) that hooked on to the ears. He does not reveal why this was the case – perhaps they made his ears sore. In any case, he patented a new design for spectacle frames, with shorter arms that ended in forks. The ends of these forks were to be provided with rounded serrated ends so that they would rest comfortably on the temples or cheek bones, and the glasses would be kept in place by a string behind the head.

In 1793 John Dalton, the new Professor of Mathematics and Natural Philosophy at the New College in Manchester, scientifically described colour-blindness for the first time. He himself was unable to tell the difference between red and green, which we now call red-green deficient, and he elegantly described his own observations of the condition. He realised that colour-blindness must be hereditary, since his brother saw things the same way as he did.

After thinking about his colour-blindness for years, Dalton became convinced that he could not distinguish between red and green because his eyeballs were tinted blue, and in a rather macabre way asked that after his death his eyes should be removed so that his theory could be proved. When he died in 1844, his body was placed in Manchester Town Hall, and 40,000 people filed past to pay their last respects. But he was wrong about his eyeballs: when they were removed they turned out not to be tinged at all. We now know colour-blindness is caused by a missing gene. However, for many years it was called Daltonism, after him.

Tansley's design for spectacles (1899)

10 Fun and games

The Victorians seem to have taken everything rather seriously, even themselves. Life should be regular and organised, and even their games had to be played by the book. As a result they took out many patents for toys and games, and even some for crackers!

An electrical engineer called James Ernest Spagnoletti, of Ealing, must have been dissatisfied with conventional Christmas crackers, since he invented a new type:

> I form my improved cracker, of any suitable material, in the form of what is known as a 'wish bone' or in the form of an horse shoe, one side or arm of which is weakened at any desired spot; to the other side or arm of the 'wish bone' or horse shoe I attach, in any desired manner, the usual prize or gift which is suitably enclosed. The explosive or detonating material is contained in a strip of paper or other suitable material connected to each side or arm of the 'wish bone' or horse shoe, so that when the sides or arms are pulled in opposite directions, fracturing said paper or other connection, a report will take place ...

Actually I like the idea of combining the festive Christmas cracker with the old folklore idea that wishbones and horseshoes bring luck, so I am sorry that these new improved crackers failed to take over the Christmas table.

On the other hand I disapprove strongly of the designated weak spot, which is presumably built in so that a generous parent can make sure that the child at the other end gets all the 'luck' – or conversely so that greedy pigs can scoop all the prizes for themselves. What Mr Spagnoletti does not mention is the dreadful jokes; perhaps they were a later invention.

Wishbone and horseshoe crackers (1899): they just didn't have enough pull

In Kattowitz, Silesia, in the German Empire, Joseph Reidel and Rudolph Block produced a complex variation of the hoop, that quintessential Victorian toy. Their new hoop had a second hoop inside it, and a clever arrangement of little windmills, each of a spindle with two arms ending in a cup or an angled blade, so that when the hoop was bowled along the ground, the arms would spin in the slipstream.

Design for a Victorian toy: the double hoop with windmills (1899)

When I first saw the diagram for Henry Long's rowing boat I thought it was meant to be one of those fiendish exercise machines in which you are supposed to row furiously without getting anywhere. However, it turned out to be a simple toy. When you pull it along the table or the floor the chap inside appears to be rowing. He is in fact supported on a pivot, and is made to rock to and fro by a lever attached to a crank on one of the wheels. Since his arms are fixed and the oars are pivoted, the oars also move backward and forward, and he seems to be rowing. My only hesitation about buying one of these toys for my grandson is that the rower looks rather grim, like a grumpy gondolier.

John Thomas Milson Hircock, an engineer in Birmingham, had higher ambitions in designing his new rocking horse, for he claimed it would be 'very useful in teaching children and young people to attain a firm seat and also as affording considerable exercise for the body whether as a rocking horse in a room or as a galloping horse on ordinary roads or in larger buildings affording sufficient space for turning corners'. His claim continues:

> **The simplest form is that of the rocking horse which consists of a single action. In this form the horse itself is fitted underneath ... with a pivot plate ... The horse is then mounted on a cross bar which is carried by a frame ... Across the two front legs of the frame a cross shaft is mounted in bearings with a crank and pedal at each end in such a position as to enable the rider to work the pedals when sitting comfortably on the horse ...**

The pedal shaft is connected via an eccentric and a shaft to the front of the horse, so that 'when the pedal is worked by the rider motion is transferred to it ... which rocks the horse thus imitating the action of a horse'.

This sounds simple, and looks reasonable in his diagram,

Improvements in Rocking or Galloping Horses didn't quite rock on (1899)

but I wonder just how comfortable it would be to work those pedals. Horses are wide, and when you sit on one your knees are pushed well apart; the riding position is quite different from that of a cyclist. I suspect that, if the rocking horse were as wide as, say, a skinny pony, pedalling would be difficult even if it remained stationary, but in fact it would rock up and down, continually taking your feet off the pedals. However, this consideration did not stop Mr Hircock, who went on to make it a real mover.

'To add forward action to the horse the frame is mounted

upon wheels ... Then upon the pedal shaft a large sprocket wheel is fixed and a smaller one on the driving shaft which are coupled by a chain ...' The rider has reins to control the steering wheel, and is able to speed along the road with a rocking or galloping action. Perhaps this would be fun, but it sounds to me like a rather dangerous form of bicycle!

Golfing gizmos

I had not realised that the passion for golf is at least a hundred years old, since golfing gadgets feature frequently in the patent files of the nineteenth century. A relatively simple, adjustable, skidding golf tee was dreamed up by Agnes Donnelly and Grace Dods of Dumbarton and Jane Ballantyne and John Ballantyne Small of Glasgow, who wanted:

> **to lessen, in some degree, the many difficulties now experienced in shooting the ball from its resting place to destination point. Hitherto, much skill has been required for the purpose of shooting the ball, and, as a consequence, exact or skilful play has been confined to the few select or skilful players of a club. With the use of our adjustable golf tee, greater ease and more exactitude is given to the play and thus**

Crazy Golf: the Adjustable Golf Tee (1899)

the game of golf is rendered still more popular by reason of this ease and exactitude, as aforestated.

By means of our improved golf tee, with the ball poised in position and adjusted to the required height from the ground and the skid or skidding arm adjusted to the required angle and the whole spiked firmly to the ground, the player is, thereby, more easily enabled to drive the ball with greater force and with surer aim than has, hitherto, been the rule.

The idea is straightforward: you line up the springy steel tee along the direction in which you want to hit the ball, put the ball in the little cup at the top, and then wallop it with your club, using the sloping arm of the tee as a guide to bring your club head up to the ball at just the right height and at just the right angle.

There seem to me to be two drawbacks to this otherwise clever piece of apparatus. First, the patentees complain that 'exact or skilful play has been confined to the few select or skilful players of a club', but this seems to me to be a good thing. If ever anyone could invent apparatus that enabled all golfers to play with precisely the same skill then the game would become totally boring. Exact play would be tedious in the extreme. Anything that reduces the effect of skill must be bad news; for example, if every player had to fire the ball from a preset catapult on the tee, then presumably every ball would end up in almost the same place on the fairway.

Second, their sliding slope seems to be designed to get the club head both angled upward and moving upward at the moment when it hits the ball. These inventors cannot have come across the work of P.G. Tait, a scientist and a lifelong member of the Royal and Ancient Club at St Andrews, and known to his fellow members as 'the Professor'. After much observation, calculation, and testing

Save it for a rainy day: appliances for the Game of Parlour Golf (1899)

he concluded that the well-struck golf ball is enabled to fly as far as it does because it has back-spin; the angled face of all clubs sends the ball off spinning backward up to 50 times a second, and this back-spin coupled with its forward motion gives the ball lift; without this lift the ball would travel only about half as far in the air.

Tait showed that the longest drives leave the ground at an angle of about 8 degrees, and that in order to achieve this the club head must be travelling horizontally when it hits the ball. A club head sliding up this new improved golf tee, whose ramp is at about 7 degrees, would dispatch the ball into the air at roughly 15 degrees, which would make for drives that went very high, but not very far. I think I'll stick with old-fashioned tees.

A dental surgeon in Surrey, Frederick Adolphus Bellamy, invented a game of parlour golf, to be played on a table.

Each player was to have a 'club' consisting of a spoon or hook attached to a clip or ring fitting on the finger. When used for lofting – to get out of a bunker, for example – the hook faces forward, while for putting it is reversed.

The 'green' and 'hole' are made from a metal plate covered with a cloth which extends beyond the edges of the plate to lie on the table. The plate is dished so that it rises from its edges towards the centre, where there is a depression forming the 'hole'. Irregularities may be formed in the cloth or the plate to imitate rough ground. The 'bunkers' are made from sheets of cardboard folded into V-shapes and secured by hooks or wedges. In his diagram, f is the club, c is a bunker, b^2 is the hole, and a is the tee, made from an extra piece of cloth.

William Harley White of Edinburgh was a printer and publisher of *The Golfer*, and he invented a game of 'short golf' for those who were desperate to have their own course but lacked the rolling acres needed for a conventional course. He said the game could be played 'in restricted areas of ground, roofed or unroofed' – in other words, you could play indoors!

'The apparatus consists of pendant strips or tapes of hemp, cotton, wool, or other spun or woven material, or strips of leather, rubber, or other material set up to partially impede the progress of a golf ball when driven against it ...' These pendant strips were to be hung from bars and to reach the ground. The ball was to be played 'from in front of the apparatus with a full stroke, as on open ground. The ball in striking against the pendant strings or strips is partially retarded in its motion, the amount of retardation being arranged by the number of lines of strings or strips it has to pass through before reaching the other side of the apparatus.'

He suggested that there should be nine or eighteen holes, with at least three strokes for each hole, each one needing its own array of hanging strips (continued on page 120).

This idea was a long shot: apparatus for Indoor Golf (1897)

> **First, drive off tee through apparatus. Second, drive
> through green through apparatus. Third, approach
> to putting green through apparatus. … Hazards and
> bunkers can be placed about the ground between
> each apparatus …**
>
> **The line of the course can be confined by netting
> or other dividing material, and players can pass
> through the apparatus by pushing the strings or
> strips aside … The putting greens can be of turf,
> rubber, cloth, cork, linoleum or other suitable
> material. The strings or strips of apparatus may be
> more sparsely distributed in direct line of drive
> through, so as to allow the straight driving player an
> advantage of getting his ball through easier than a
> badly driven ball.**

In principle it sounds as though this game could be
playable, but I am amazed at the scale of the operation. A
course of 27 holes would require hundreds of yards of
hanging strips, and hundreds of yards of scaffolding to hang
them on, which would be enormously expensive. However,
the space would be an even greater problem. In order to be
able to play 'a full stroke' you need a minimum space of
something like four yards (3.6 metres) square, otherwise you
would always be hitting the apparatus with your club. White
claims that nine holes of (at least) three strokes each could
be fitted into a third of an acre, which is about the area of a
tennis court. What's more, in his sketch of the apparatus (see
over) he shows it set up inside what appears to be a great hall
or conservatory. I don't know many people who have halls or
conservatories covering a third of an acre, and I imagine that
people who actually own such huge rooms might well have
enough space in the grounds to lay out a real golf course.

Musical mayhem

Lacking television or even radio, Victorian families were forced to entertain themselves in the evenings, and music making was a popular pastime. Young ladies were encouraged to play the piano, and a problem that must have beset most households was how to turn the pages of the music without a helpful sister standing patiently by your shoulder. Henry Benjamin Wing spotted this problem, and patented a simple solution: small metal clips (or gummed tags of stiff paper) to attach to the edge of the page, so that it could easily be flipped over between notes. As he pointed out: 'The clips can be attached one to each leaf at a different point and the ends project so that they can be seized by the tips of the fingers. As there is only one clip for each leaf there is no danger of two leaves being turned accidentally.'

However, this was far too simple for Johann Schweinfurth II and Heinrich Bechdolf, who designed a wondrous machine to do the same job. The mechanism is complicated to explain, but should have been simple to operate, since pressing a foot pedal once would turn one page,

This invention was in the wrong key: the means for Turning the Leaves of Music (1899)

pressing again would turn the next, and so on. In fact this looks to me like a slightly advanced version of the machine invented by Augustin Lajarrige in 1887, which turned the pages of music at the nudge of the pianist's knee. If I were a pianist, I'd like to have one of these – and yet I have never seen a pianist use anything like it.

This invention was obviously missing the key to success: the Appliance for Turning Over Music defies explanation (1899)

Suffering for your art: this finger-supporting device for this budding pianist looks like torture – small wonder no one wanted to play along! (1881)

In 1881 Benjamin Atkins of Cincinnati, Ohio, produced a painful-looking device intended to hold the pianist's fingers horizontal, as far as the second joint. This, he claimed, would improve the player's touch and allow more rapid fingering, although it looks to me as though this chunk of machinery would slow you down and rapidly make your arms tired.

Finally, not content with the normal musical instruments at their disposal, enterprising musicians have invented dozens more, with varying degrees of complexity and success. In 1895 Professor Bruno Wollenhaupt of New York made a new violin with 12 extra strings inside, covering an octave in semitones. These were intended to resonate with the normal strings, greatly enriching the tone and volume of the

One-man band: the combined cello-piano and viola-piano were not bound for musical stardom (1893)

instrument (although many parents find normal violins quite loud enough!), and could be damped by the violinist with a slight movement of the chin.

In 1893 a cello teacher, Mr de Vlaminck, depressed by his students' incompetence at getting accurate pitch with their left hands, produced a combination cello-piano, in which the left hand plays a keyboard, which frets the strings precisely, while the right hand bows the strings in the usual way. He claimed that the usual effects could be obtained with the bow, and the keyboard provides the accuracy of tone which has been set once and for all. The keys are so perfectly linked to the hammers resting on the strings that it is even possible to produce the slight tremolo associated with playing with feeling!

Meanwhile, in London, John Matthias Augustus Stroh invented an entirely new instrument, in which the body of a violin with its sounding board was replaced by a frame attached to a drumhead fitted with a trumpet-shaped resonance tube. There is a direct connection between the violin bridge and the diaphragm, so that vibrations from the strings are passed directly to the diaphragm, and its resonance is amplified by the tube. I find it hard to imagine what this would have sounded like.

Seriously out of tune: this instrument was quickly left out of the orchestra! (1899)

FIG.1.

Further reading

Brown, G. I., *The Guinness History of Inventions*, Guinness 1996

Clarke, Donald (ed), *The Encyclopedia of Inventions*, Marshall Cavendish 1977

Derry, T. K. & Williams, Trevor I., *A Short History of Technology*, Oxford UP 1960, Dover 1993

de Vries, Leonard, *Victorian Inventions*, John Murray 1971

Harris, Melvin, *The ITN Book of Firsts*, Michael O'Mara 1994

Hart-Davis, Adam & Bader, Paul, *The Local Heroes Book of British Ingenuity*, Sutton 1997

Hart-Davis, Adam & Bader, Paul, *More Local Heroes*, Sutton 1998

Hart-Davis, Adam, *Thunder, Flush, and Thomas Crapper*, Michael O'Mara 1997

Robertson, Patrick, *The Shell Book of Firsts*, Ebury Press & Michael Joseph 1974

Tibbals, Geoff, *The Guinness Book of Innovations*, Guinness 1994

On the subject of perpetual motion, there is a mass of material both in *Encyclopaedia Britannica* 9th edn, 1885, and on the Internet. For inventions in detail nothing can beat the original patents, which can be consulted at the old patent office in London, or in various other places around the country.

Picture Acknowledgements

Jolyon Troscianko: 9, 35, 43, 45, 46, 47, 67, 69

The Patent Office: 8, 12, 19, 41, 62, 64, 66, 70, 77, 81, 85, 88, 89, 91, 99, 105, 108, 109, 111, 113, 114, 116, 118, 122, 123, 124

Scientific American: 11, 24, 27, 31, 36, 37, 55, 60, 66, 84, 93, 102, 123, 124

La Nature: 86, 106

De Natuur: 1, 8, 28, 32, 42, 96

Bristol Museums & Art Gallery: 100, 101

Dover images: 54

All other pictures were provided by the author.

Index

All Michael O'Mara titles are available by post from:

Bookpost, PO Box 29, Douglas, Isle of Man IM99 1BQ

Credit cards accepted.
Telephone: 01624 677237
Fax: 01624 670923
Email: bookshop@enterprise.net
Internet: www.bookpost.co.uk

Free postage and packing in the UK.

Other Michael O'Mara Humour titles:

All Men Are Bastards – ISBN 1-85479-387-X pb £3.99
The Book of Urban Legends – ISBN 1-85479-932-0 pb £3.99
The Complete Book of Farting – ISBN 1-85479-440-X pb £4.99
Complete Crap – ISBN 1-85479-313-6 pb £3.99
The Ultimate Book of Farting – ISBN 1-85479-596-1 hb £5.99
The Ultimate Insult – ISBN 1-85479-288-1 pb £5.99
Wicked Cockney Rhyming Slang – ISBN 1-85479-386-1 pb £3.99
Wicked Geordie English – ISBN 1-85479-342-X pb £3.99
Wicked Scouse English – ISBN 1-84317-006-X pb £3.99
The Wicked Wit of Jane Austen – ISBN 1-85479-652-6 hb £9.99
The Wicked Wit of Winston Churchill – ISBN 1-85479-529-5 hb £9.99
The Wicked Wit of Charles Dickens – ISBN 1-85479-047-1 hb £9.99
The Wicked Wit of Oscar Wilde – ISBN 1-85479-542-2 hb £9.99
The World's Stupidest Criminals – ISBN 1-85479-879-0 pb £3.99
The World's Stupidest Graffiti – ISBN 1-85479-876-6 pb £3.99
The World's Stupidest Inventions – ISBN 1-84317-036-1 pb £5.99
The World's Stupidest Laws – ISBN 1-85479-549-X pb £3.99
The World's Stupidest Men – ISBN 1-85479-508-2 pb £3.99
The World's Stupidest Signs – ISBN 1-85479-555-4 pb £3.99
More of the World's Stupidest Signs – ISBN 1-84317-032-9 pb £4.99
The World's Stupidest Last Words – ISBN 1-84317-021-3 pb £4.99
Shite's Unoriginal Miscellany – ISBN 1-84317-064-7 hb £9.99